Awards & REWARDS for K-3

Certificates,
Badges,
Crafts and More

Written by Carrie J. Boyko and Julie B. Rodgers

Illustrated by Cara H. Bradshaw, Gary Hoover and Veronica Terrill

Teaching & Learning Company

1204 Buchanan St., P.O. Box 10
Carthage, IL 62321-0010

This book belongs to

_____

Cover photo by Images and More Photography

Copyright © 1999, Teaching & Learning Company

ISBN No. 1-57310-183-4

Printing No. 98765432

Teaching & Learning Company
1204 Buchanan St., P.O. Box 10
Carthage, IL 62321-0010

Dedication

To Cindy Brown for giving Brent the right start, and especially to Connie Glover for believing in him and showing me how to motivate him.

Carrie J. Boyko

In memory of my dad, Herb Brenner.

Julie B. Rodgers

Acknowledgements

The authors would like to acknowledge the help of many teachers and parents in the central Florida area. Their support and ideas have impacted this book tremendously. We especially want to mention the many faculty members of Clay Springs Elementary who shared their innovative programs and positive ideas with us. Thank you to all who helped in even a small way; you made a difference!

Table of Contents

TLC10183 Copyright © Teaching & Learning Company, Carthage, IL 62321-0010

Section 4: The Sciences

Section 5: Special Area Classes

Art

Music

Physical Education

Media

Computer Skills

Section 6: Preschool/Kindergarten

Dear Teacher,

A few years ago, Carrie's first-grade son arrived home on the last day of school with a fistful of certificates which he proceeded to stuff into the trash. Appalled by this waste of a teacher's motivation efforts, she retrieved them and asked why he didn't wish to keep them. His reply was, "They're boring! What fun is a certificate?"

As we (the authors) talked about that episode, we realized that he was right. Certificates are more of a tool to communicate with home and to give recognition. They really don't serve well to motivate most kids. Awards & Rewards was born of this renaissance, with five goals in mind:

1. Materials are to be quick and easy to use.

2. Rewards will include many fun activities and crafts.

3. Additional ideas will be included to help both teachers and parents with motivation in various areas.

4. Awards will improve communication between school and home.

5. Many rewards will encourage interaction between parent and child.

Take note of the border around this letter. Each time you see this border, the contents are addressed especially to you, the teacher. Watch for these informative Teacher Tips sections throughout this book.

Sincerely,

Carrie & Julie

Carrie J. Boyko and Julie B. Rodgers

To help you and your students get the most out of this book, here are a few tips on how to use it:

- We recommend that you encourage your students to bring in and share their completed crafts or activities. Perhaps you could offer a sticker for those which come back to school for a viewing. This will give you one last opportunity to praise the student for his good work, and will show other kids the fun activities they will receive if they exhibit the same skills or behaviors.

- Be sure to sign and date each award when given. This will be valuable information to parents like Julie and Carrie, who each have three children, and often find papers get mixed up on the kitchen table. Have you ever had a paper come home, only to find that none of your children claim it? We have!

- Please pass on to another teacher any sections of this book which you will not use in your own classroom. Your fellow teacher will appreciate your generosity and return the favor someday.

vii

Before copying the original in this book, check the copy key at the top of the page. The following simple symbols will tell you whether to copy on white or colored paper, or whether to copy on white or colored card stock. Of course, in the absence of colored paper, white will always do in a pinch. After all, it is also fun for the kids to color their awards.

While most of the rewards and activities herein need only paper, crayons, scissors, tape and glue to be completed, a few of the awards require that you send an item or two home. In each case, these are common classroom items, which most homes aren't equipped with, such as brass or crepe paper. These simple symbols follow:

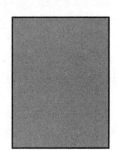

| White Copy Paper | Colored Copy Paper | White Card Stock | Colored Card Stock |

 Brass Fastener

 Crepe Paper

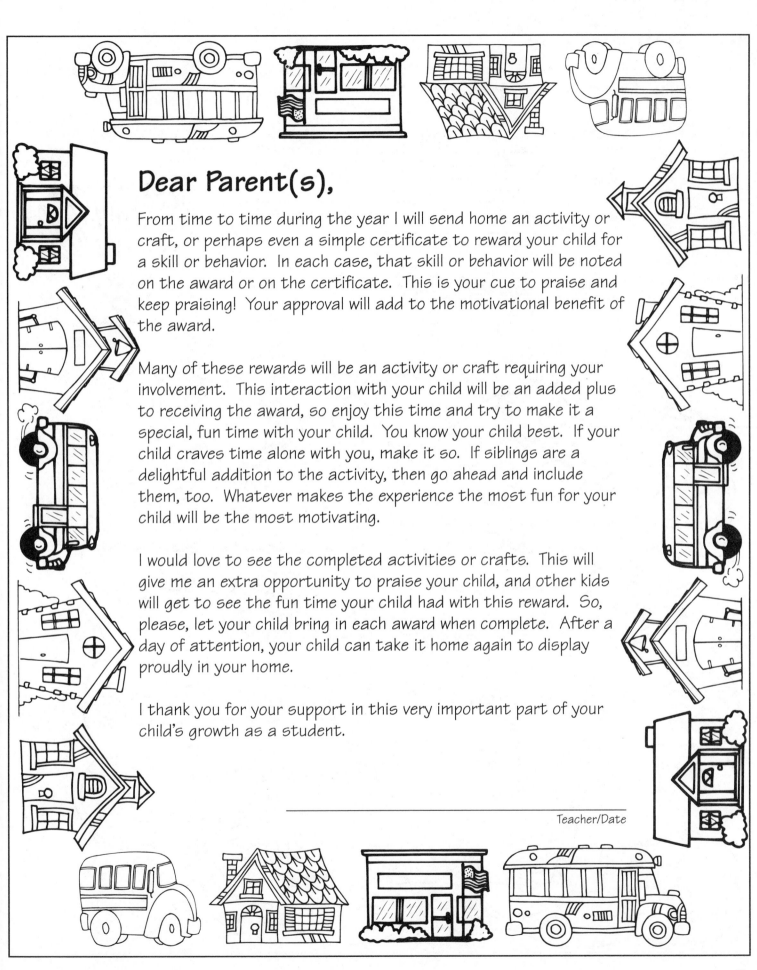

Dear Parent(s),

From time to time during the year I will send home an activity or craft, or perhaps even a simple certificate to reward your child for a skill or behavior. In each case, that skill or behavior will be noted on the award or on the certificate. This is your cue to praise and keep praising! Your approval will add to the motivational benefit of the award.

Many of these rewards will be an activity or craft requiring your involvement. This interaction with your child will be an added plus to receiving the award, so enjoy this time and try to make it a special, fun time with your child. You know your child best. If your child craves time alone with you, make it so. If siblings are a delightful addition to the activity, then go ahead and include them, too. Whatever makes the experience the most fun for your child will be the most motivating.

I would love to see the completed activities or crafts. This will give me an extra opportunity to praise your child, and other kids will get to see the fun time your child had with this reward. So, please, let your child bring in each award when complete. After a day of attention, your child can take it home again to display proudly in your home.

I thank you for your support in this very important part of your child's growth as a student.

_____
Teacher/Date

☐ Helpful to Others

Dear Parent(s),

Your child has been a joy to have in class. This simple craft award is a reward for helpfulness. Please assist your child with this craft and enjoy your time together. Thank you!

Fan

_____
Teacher/Date

1. Cut out the fan below.
2. Accordion-fold the paper.

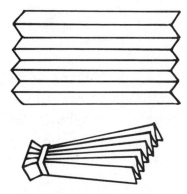

3. Squeeze the bottom together and tape closed.

4. Fan out the top and keep cool!

"FANTASTIC HELPER"

This

RESPECT

award is presented to

_____

for respectful and courteous
treatment of others.

_____
Teacher/Date

Congratulations to _____

for receiving the

Good
Friend
Award!

_____
Teacher/Date

Dear Parent(s),

Your child has demonstrated the skill of good listening and is being rewarded with this fun craft to do at home. I hope you will enjoy this project, as the time spent with you is also part of the reward. Thank you!

_____
Teacher/Date

Elephant Mask

1. Cut out and color the elephant's ears and trunk.
2. Glue the ears and trunk onto a paper plate as shown.
3. Draw the elephant's eyes onto the paper plate.
4. Punch holes at left and right as shown.
5. Tie on a piece of string, yarn, ribbon or rubber bands to be used to tie on your mask.
6. Have fun and congratulations on being a good listener, just like your new friend with the big ears!

Elephant Trunk

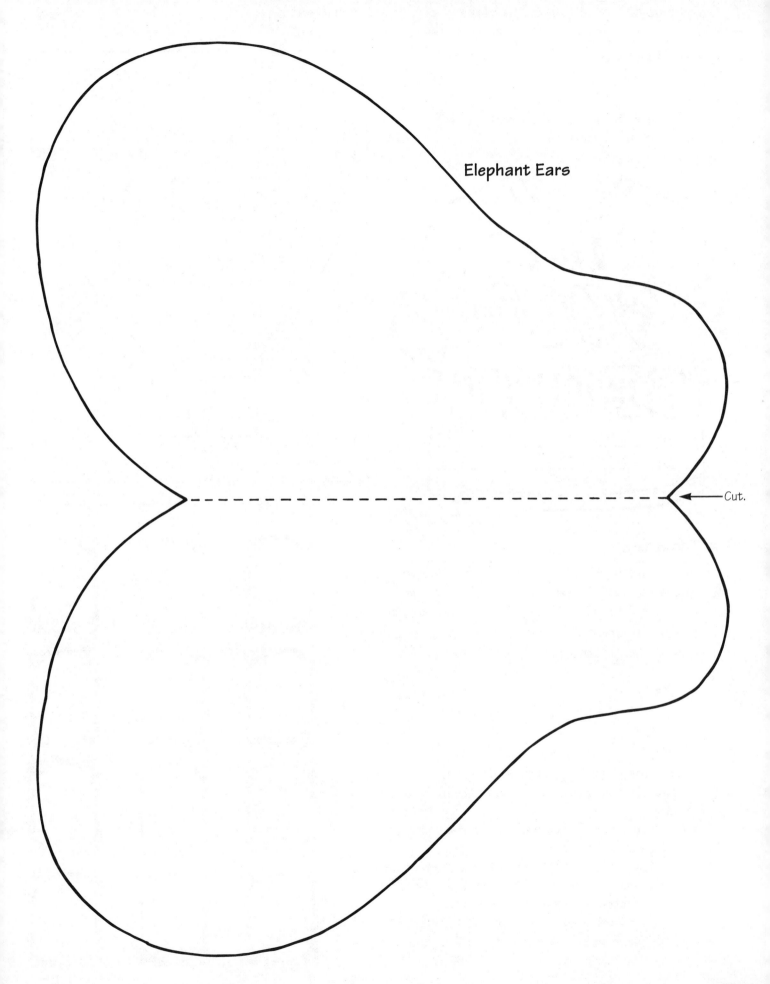

Elephant Ears

Cut.

Button or Necklace

1. Cut out and color.
2. Pin on, or . . .
3. Make a hole in the top and place string or yarn through to make a necklace.
4. Tie on and wear proudly!

Teacher/Date

Color by number: 1 = orange, 2 = blue, 3 = yellow

Teacher/Date

Dear Parent(s),

Your child is being rewarded for good participation. Enjoy playing this matching card game together. All you need is a deck of cards for this fun game which will help to build your child's memory skills. Play it often, and be generous with your praise for good class participation.

_____
Teacher/Date

Concentration

1. Shuffle cards thoroughly and deal out 12 cards, facedown as shown. Continue to deal on top of these cards, making 12 piles.
2. Players take turns turning over two cards, trying to find matches (Jacks, 10s, aces, etc.).
3. If a match is turned up, the player keeps the matched cards and gets another turn. Play moves to another player if no match can be made.
4. When all cards are used or when your child tires of the game, the game ends. Have your child count the matches.

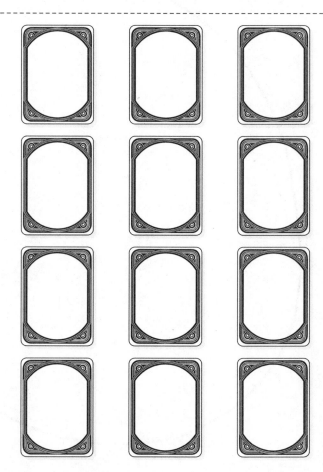

Scroll

1. Cut out scroll.
2. Roll up scroll.
3. Tie a bow around the scroll with ribbon or yarn.

HEAR YE! HEAR YE!

Let it be known that

_____

is a

Good Problem Solver!

_____
Teacher/Date

To my family: Please ask me about our problem and how I solved it creatively.

| ■ | Follows Directions Well | □ | Good Example in Line |

Dear Parent(s),

Your child does a very good job at following directions. Reinforce this wonderful behavior by giving some positive attention at home, too. Applause is optional!

Please help your child read the instructions at the right, one at a time. When the directions have been successfully followed, please praise the good job. Thanks for your help!

_____
Teacher/Date

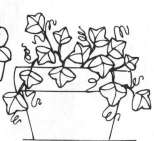

Directions to Follow

1. Put your book bag or back-pack away where it belongs.
2. Write your name three times on a piece of paper.
3. Draw a picture of something that makes you happy on the back of this award.
4. Hug your parents.
5. Enjoy the praise. You have earned it.

- -

Dear Parent(s),

Your child has earned this fun craft for being a good example in line. You should be very proud.

Help your child cut out and color this walking puppet. You can take turns playing with it and laughing as your child creates fun ways to use it. Enjoy!

_____
Teacher/Date

Cut out. Cut out.

16

Dear Parent(s),

Your child has earned a reward for good behavior.

This craft can be completed with your help at home. Relish this time together, as it is also part of the reward. Have fun!

_____

Teacher/Date

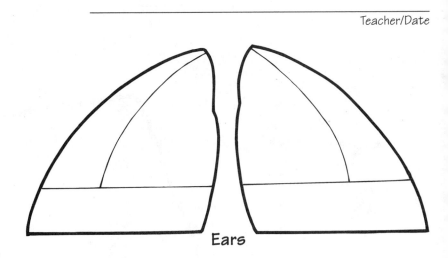

Ears

Paper Bag Puppet

1. Color the kitten's parts.
2. Cut out the kitten's parts.
3. Glue onto a paper lunch bag as shown in the sample above. Glue the nose at the fold of the kitten's head and the mouth on the body below.
4. Maybe your kitten can recite kitten rhymes or sing kitten songs. Enjoy!

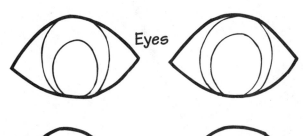

Eyes

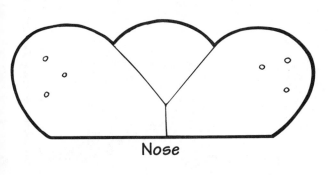

Nose

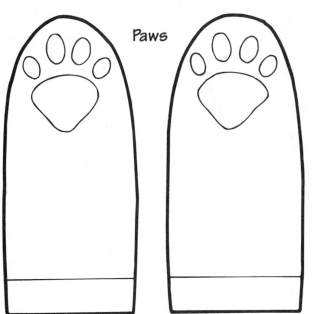

Paws

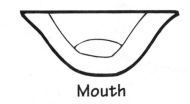

Mouth

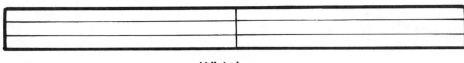

Whiskers

Dear Parent(s),

This decorative kite craft is a reward to your child for following rules. You and your child can make this craft together as an added reward. Have fun, and be sure to praise great behavior.

_____
Teacher/Date

Kite

1. Cut out and color or decorate the kite below.
2. Add a 2" (.61 m) long tail of yarn, string or ribbon.
3. Tie short pieces of tail material onto the tail.
4. Hang up and enjoy!

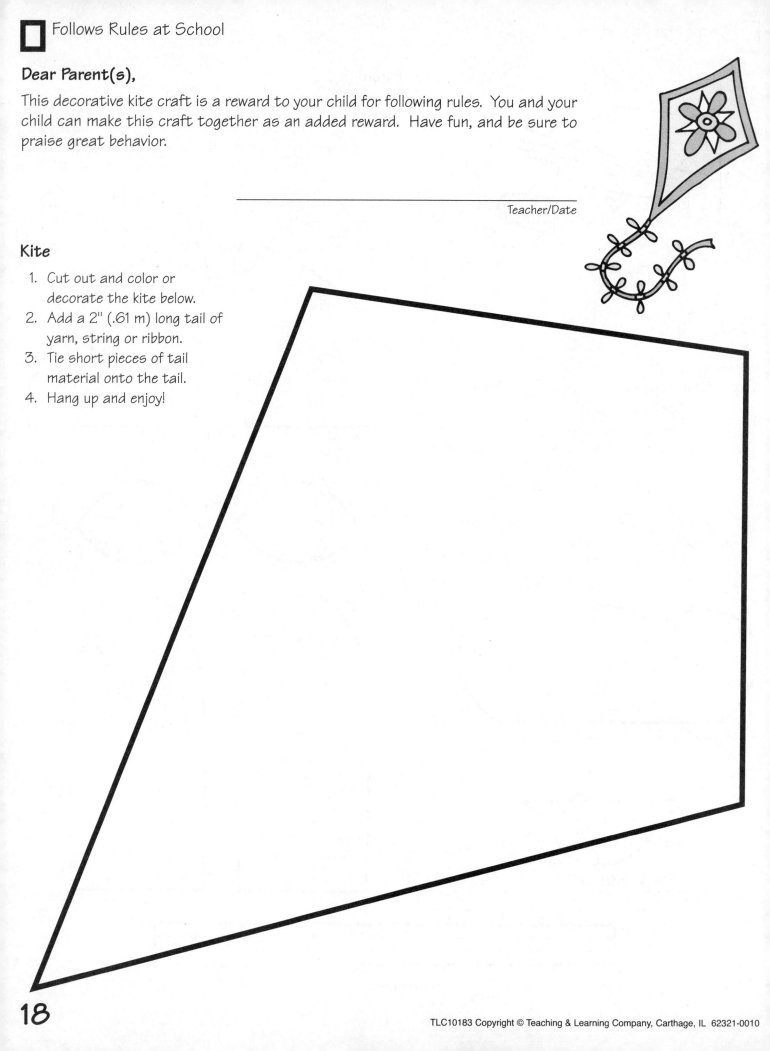

Ideas for a Happy Classroom

- Give your students the five As: *acceptance, attention, appreciation, affirmation and affection.*

- Listen to the students. Hear what they are saying. This models respect, an important quality for children to experience.

- Greet your students each morning at the door with a hug and a smile. Let them know you are happy to see them.

- Provide lots of positive reinforcement and praise. Catch them being good!

- Encourage your students to help one another. Use peer tutors and peer counseling in your classroom.

- Have a sense of humor. Smile! It's okay to joke around with the kids!

Basics of Discipline

- Implement specific classroom rules, along with rewards and consequences.

- State the rules in a positive way. Post them in a highly visible place in the classroom.

- Explain these rules, consequences and rewards to parents at Open House or in a conference.

- Be calm when disciplining a child.

- Discipline a child in private rather than in front of others.

- Repeat and model desired behavior.

- Try having class meetings to work out problems. (Ex: problems walking in line, problems with picking on others, etc.)

Rewarding Good Behavior

- Mail positive notes home.

- Take a moment to call home with a positive message of thanks for good behavior.

- Eat lunch with a specific child (or the whole class!) as a reward.

- As a reward, have a special button to wear or special chair to sit in. A special bulletin board might also be useful.

- Hand out homework passes.

- Give free time or extra computer time.

- Announce special accomplishments on the morning announcements.

Parent Pointers

Dear Parent(s),

As parents of a young child, you no doubt know the challenge of helping your child learn to get along with others. Improved social development will help in every aspect of your child's education and, therefore, deserves its share of effort. Following are a few tips you might find useful in working on these areas. Please feel free to contact me if you have any questions or concerns.

_____
Teacher/Date

- At a very young age children should learn the *Golden Rule*. Discuss it often, as your child's growing sense of understanding blossoms. Whenever a situation is encountered where your child seeks your advice, this should be the guiding principle for the decision.

- To be mastered, many social skills require repeated practice. You can facilitate this merely by offering encouragement and opportunities—friends over to play.

- As parents, you must accept that early friendships and experiences with peers will be stormy and sometimes painful. You can help with guidance before and after episodes of difficulty, but it is often best not to intervene in the midst of a skirmish, unless physical injury becomes a possibility.

- Children often form alliances—"them vs. us"—which can prove emotionally harmful to the losers. These situations require constant supervision and monitoring to assure that children are encouraged to treat one another with respect.

- Remind your child that no one likes a bully. Friendships are built on *give and take*, not *push*.

- Setting and enforcing rules in your home will help your child understand and accept the rules at school.

- Learning when to talk and when to be quiet is especially tough for energetic youngsters. Ask your child to tell you some listening rules. This should generate a good discussion of times and places that are inappropriate for talking.

- A student who tattles frequently often becomes disliked by other kids, as well as a nuisance to the teacher. Help your child understand that there is no reason to be a police officer. Only tattle when someone's safety is at risk.

- Playing cards and board games at home will allow your child to experience losing in a safe, family atmosphere. This way your child will realize that it is okay to lose a game. This exposure will help with better acceptance of losing at school and with friends.

- Catch your child doing something good and be sure to praise or reward.

☐ Neat Schoolwork

Dear Parent(s),

These funny glasses to make are a reward for your child's neat schoolwork. In addition to your praise, your child will enjoy this time together. Being one-on-one with you is the ultimate reward. Thank you!

_____
Teacher/Date

Funny Glasses

1. Color and cut out all three parts of the glasses below.
2. Fold the sides of the glasses along the fold line and glue, tape or staple the tab inside the top, front corners of the glasses as shown.
3. Have fun!

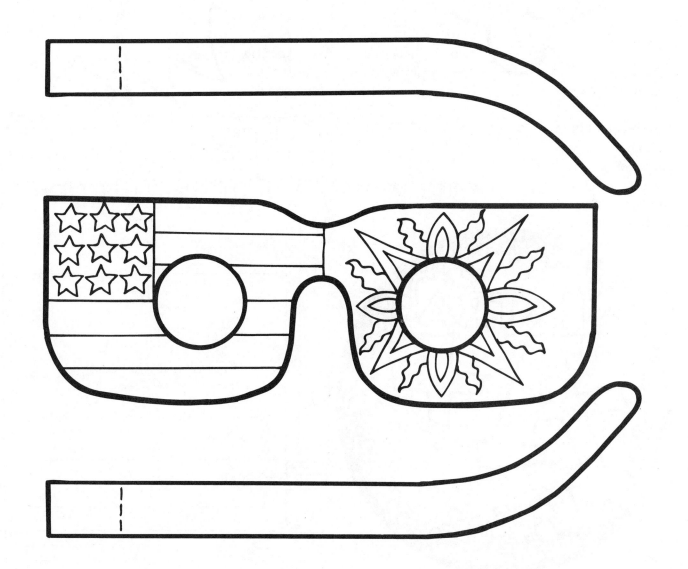

☐ Neat Work Area   ☐ Perfect Attendance   ☐ Extra Effort   ☐ Neat Handwriting

Pencil Topper

1. Cut out and color.

2. Cut small slits where shown.

3. Proudly display your award on your pencil.

I keep a NEAT Work Area!

Award Ribbon

1. Cut out.
2. Color.
3. Wear your ribbon with pride!

pERFEct Attendance!

_____
Teacher/Date

Button or Necklace

1. Cut out and color.
2. Pin on, or . . .
3. Make a hole in the top and place string or yarn through to make a necklace.
4. Tie on and wear proudly!

EXTRA A+ Effort

CONGRATULATIONS to
_____
for
Neat Handwriting!
Check out this sample:
_____
_____
_____
_____

Teacher/Date

Teacher Tips

Attach a photocopy of the chart header below on a photocopy of the chart grid on page 128. Each time a student turns in homework on time, place a sticker or stamp in one box on the grid, or initial it.

You can use these with select students when needed, or make one for the whole class. They are particularly effec-tive at the beginning of the school year, to get the kids started on the right track. You may also find this approach helpful near year end when the kids get a bit dis-tracted by the summer fun ahead.

Three coupon choices are offered below, but feel free to make your own if a particular incentive works well with your students. The better the motivation, the better the program will work. Good luck!

Homework on Time

Teacher Helper for a Day	Sit by a Friend	No Homework
Teacher Helper for a Day	Sit by a Friend	No Homework
Teacher Helper for a Day	Sit by a Friend	No Homework

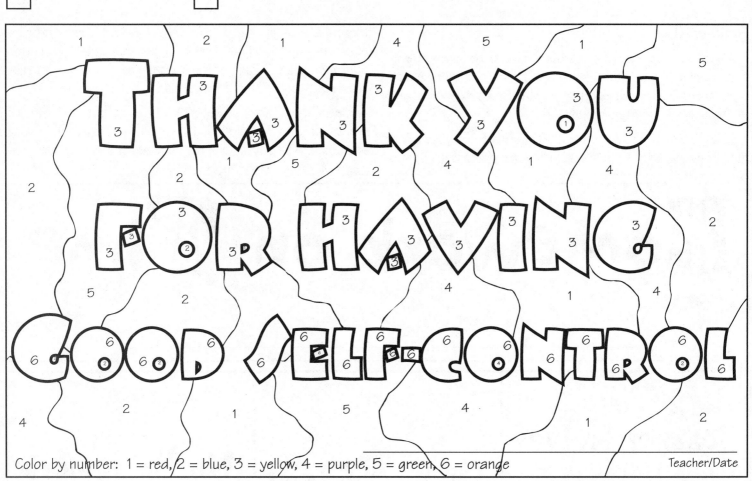

Color by number: 1 = red, 2 = blue, 3 = yellow, 4 = purple, 5 = green, 6 = orange   Teacher/Date

Dear Parent(s),

Your child is receiving this finger puppet craft award for completing classwork on time. Please praise this effort and enjoy doing this craft as an additional bonus. Have fun!

_____
Teacher/Date

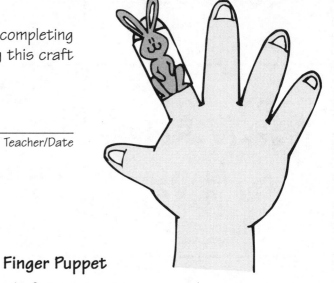

Finger Puppet

1. Cut out.
2. Color or decorate.
3. Roll into a cylinder and tape the back.
4. Let your new friend announce your good news to the family.

24

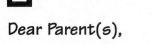 Arrives at School on Time ⦿ ☐ Never Gives Up

Dear Parent(s),

Your child is being rewarded for arriving at school on time. This craft will be fun for you to make together and will be an enjoyable way to review time-telling skills. You can help connect time to the real world by having your child show you what time things happen. (Ex: bedtime, dinnertime, etc.) Have fun!

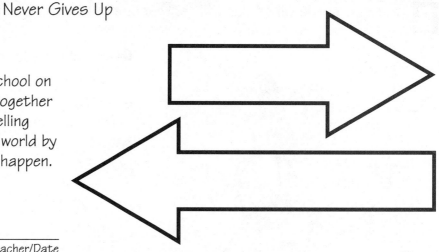

_____
Teacher/Date

Clock

1. Color and cut out the numbers and clock hands.
2. Glue the numbers in their proper places on a paper plate.
3. Use a brass fastener to connect the hands through the center of the clock.
4. When you're through, set the clock to the time you finished. Good job!

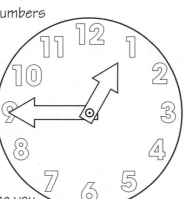

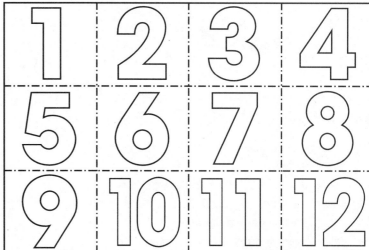

Dear Parent(s),

You have taught the value of perseverance quite well. Your child is being rewarded with a craft for demonstrating this skill. Please help make this simple headband. This time with you will be an important part of the reward. Thank you!

_____
Teacher/Date

Headband

1. Cut two strips off the long side of a plain piece of paper—any color.
2. Tape or staple them together to fit your head.
3. Color and cut out the headband sign below.
4. Glue it to the headband and wear proudly.

NEVER GIVE UP!

Dear Parent(s),

As a reward for good participation in class activities, your child is receiving this puppet craft to make at home with you. As you work on this craft, be sure to praise your child for good participation. Have fun!

_____

Teacher/Date

Finger Puppet

1. Cut out the bear and the two strips for finger loops.
2. Tape the strips into finger loops.
3. Tape the finger loops onto the back of the bear, at the top of his legs.
4. Slide your fingers down into the loops toward the bear's feet and make him walk.

☐ Good Lunchtime Manners   ▣ Understands Eating Healthy

Dear Parent(s),

Your child is being rewarded for good lunchtime manners with this place marker craft. Please help make the place markers and use them at your next family meal.

Your praise for good behavior will be an added bonus to this reward, and so will the time spent together on this craft. Thank you!

_____
Teacher/Date

Fold here.

Place Markers

1. Cut out the place marker above. Use it as a pattern to make as many as you need.
2. Write each family member's name on a marker.
3. Decorate or color for a festive table at your next family meal. Have fun!

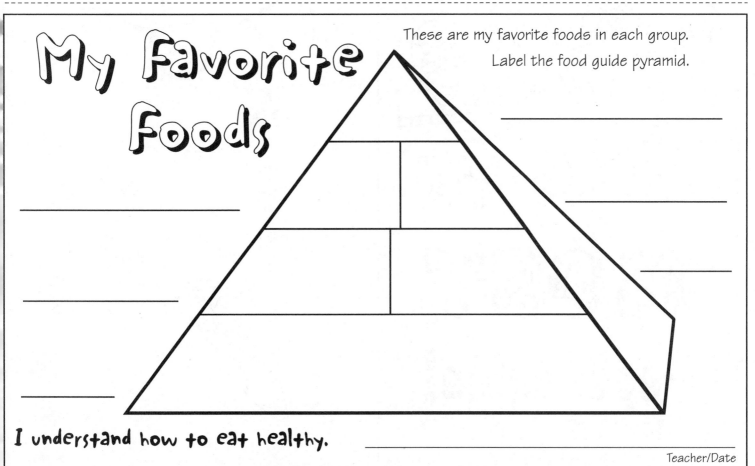

These are my favorite foods in each group.
Label the food guide pyramid.

My Favorite Foods

I understand how to eat healthy. _____

Teacher/Date

27

TLC10183 Copyright © Teaching & Learning Company, Carthage, IL 62321-0010

☐ Most Dependable   ☐ Uses Inside Voice

Pencil Topper

1. Cut out and color.
2. Cut small slits where shown.
3. Proudly display your award on your pencil.

Cut along dotted lines.
Color and hang up.

I Am Certified

MOST
Dependable!

_____
Teacher/Date

Work Habits

- Instilling good work habits in your students will require diligent effort on your part in praising and rewarding students for desired behaviors.

- Modeling the habits you desire is the first step in demonstrating your expectations of the children. After all, we cannot expect them to be organized or punctual if we are not.

- To assist with building a habit of using planners or assignment sheets, be sure to provide adequate time for entries each day. Then check these entries and praise or reward their efforts accordingly. Additionally, having parents sign the planner each night will get them involved in supervising the child's use of the planner. No more excuses!

- Have your children practice proofreading regularly to create a habit. Try offering an extra incentive for thorough proofreading.

- When introducing your students' first few long-term assignments (more than three days until due), give a suggested schedule for completion. Ask your students to offer reasons why the entire assignment cannot be done in one day.

- When study time is given in class, allow students to pair up when possible. Remind them to encourage their partners.

- You don't have to struggle to read messy homework. Ask the students to rewrite it neatly. Offer rewards for completion to your specifications. Praise lavishly when successful and remind them each day to keep up the good work.

- Often children who lack self-control feel that they are being controlled. You can give them a sense of power by offering choices and teaching the concept of total responsibility. You must help them understand that if they misbehave, it is because they choose to. They have the power to choose to behave. Once they understand this, self-control begins to take care of itself.

Parent Pointers

Dear Parent(s),

Helping your child develop good work habits, at school and at home, is one of the most important life skills you can give. As I am often asked for ideas on developing such skills, I am attaching a few ideas to help you get started. Let me know if I can help further.

_____
Teacher/Date

Homework Hints

- Every child is different. Some need playtime when they arrive home to blow off steam before refocusing on schoolwork. Contrarily, others need to finish their homework immediately upon arrival at home before they lose focus and cannot regain it. You know your child better than anyone else; let this knowledge be your guide to scheduling time for homework.

- Homework must be accomplished in the best atmosphere for total concentration—no phone, friends, TV or radio. Often with younger children, your help is crucial and may require that you work near them.

- In order to maximize your child's independence, review each assignment thoroughly before beginning. Pride of accomplishment will be the result of independent work.

- If you have a child who procrastinates with homework, try offering an incentive to be given when the homework is finished.

- Remember that homework should be an experience in learning, not an experience in frustration. Often this requires that you help your child with homework.

- With memorization kinds of homework, like vocabulary and spelling, begin as soon as the assignment is given and work in small amounts each day, reviewing the previously learned material.

- There is nothing worse than working hard on a homework assignment, only to leave it behind the next morning. Help your child choose a place to put all school materials when finished.

- The beginning of long-term assignments will be a tough new challenge for your child. Help plan time to spread out the project.

- Do not condone messy or incorrect work. Redoing a few assignments completed carelessly will show him your commitment to this principle.

- When homework is done, your most important job begins. It is very important that you review and check your child's homework. Your child needs to see where mistakes are and to correct them (with you) to understand the skill.

CONGRATULATIONS!

on _____

_____

_____

to

_____

Teacher/Date

Pencil Topper

1. Cut out and color.
2. Cut small slits where shown.
3. Proudly display your award on your pencil.

Congratulations!

to _____

for **Achievement** in

_____

_____
Teacher/Date

Button or Necklace

1. Cut out and color.
2. Pin on, or . . .
3. Make a hole in the top and place string or yarn through to make a necklace.
4. Tie on and wear proudly!

This award is for *Achievement*

in _____

_____

I'm Sailing High!

I learned to

_____

today!

Teacher/Date

I remembered to _____ TODAY!

Teacher/Date

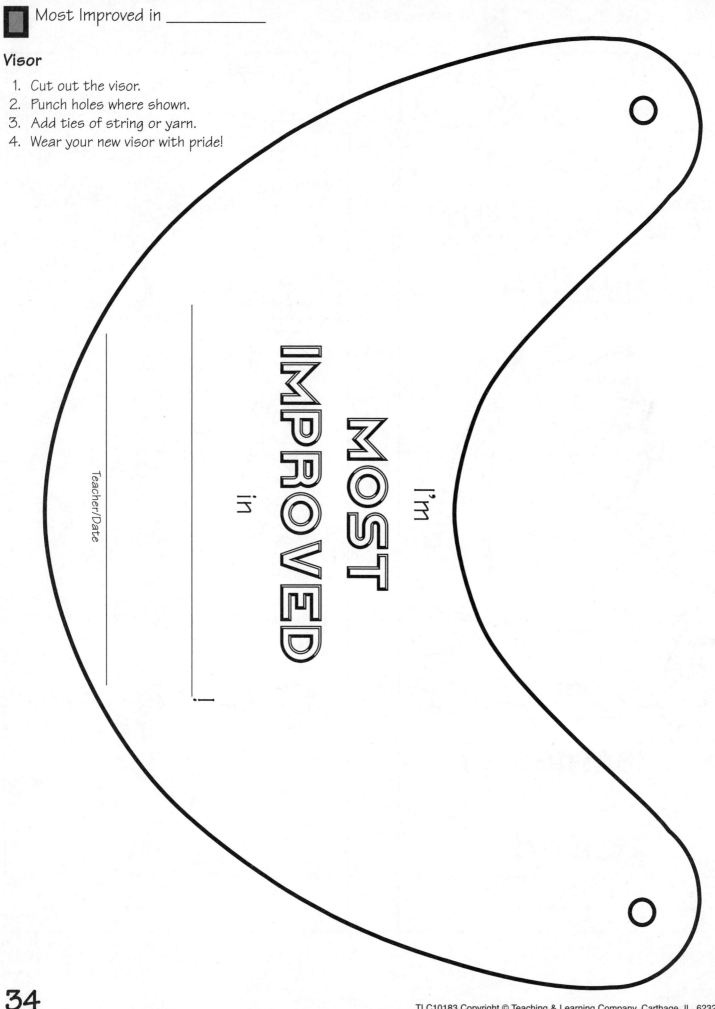

■ Most Improved in _____

Visor

1. Cut out the visor.
2. Punch holes where shown.
3. Add ties of string or yarn.
4. Wear your new visor with pride!

I'm MOST IMPROVED in _____

Teacher/Date

GOOD JOB, ___!

You are the Student of the Week!

Teacher/Date

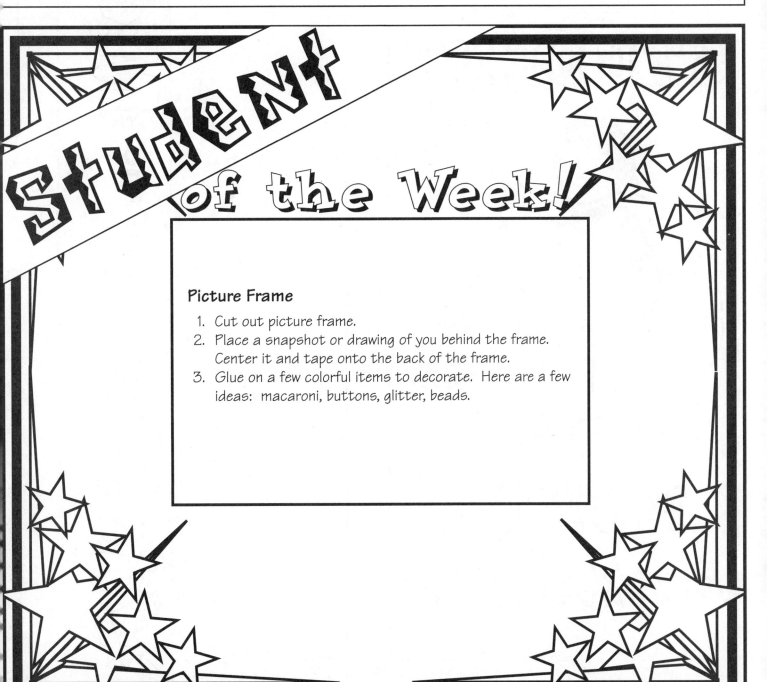

Picture Frame

1. Cut out picture frame.
2. Place a snapshot or drawing of you behind the frame. Center it and tape onto the back of the frame.
3. Glue on a few colorful items to decorate. Here are a few ideas: macaroni, buttons, glitter, beads.

1. Cut out.
2. Write name on desk sign.
3. Decorate, if desired.
4. Laminate, if possible.
5. Display proudly!

Teacher/Date

Fold here.

MONTH of the Student

Cut along dotted lines.
Color and hang up.

STUDENT

of the

MONTH
Resides Here!

Teacher/Date

☐ Good Citizen of the Week ☐ Good Citizen of the Week ☐ Good Citizen of the Month

Button or Necklace

1. Cut out and color.
2. Pin on, or . . .
3. Make a hole in the top and place string or yarn through to make a necklace.
4. Tie on and wear proudly!

Pencil Topper

1. Cut out and color.

2. Cut small slits where shown.

3. Proudly display your award on your pencil.

Dear Parent(s),

In recognition of being such a good citizen this month, your child has received this Uncle Sam finger puppet craft to make at home with you. We hope you will enjoy this special time with your special child!

_____

Teacher/Date

Finger Puppet

1. Cut out puppet.
2. Color with crayons or markers.
3. Tape into a tube on your finger.
4. Have fun singing patriotic songs or giving speeches!

Desk Sign

1. Cut out and color.
2. Write name on desk sign.
3. Decorate, if desired.
4. Display proudly on your desk.

Fold here.

_____

GOOD
CITIZEN
of the MONTH

_____

Teacher/Date

has received the

HERO AWARD

for an outstanding or courageous act.

Congratulations!

Teacher/Date

Dear Parent(s),

Please help your child make this alligator puppet. It is a reward for being so delightful in class. Have fun together and enjoy this project.

_____

Paper Bag Puppet

1. Turn a paper lunch bag upside down. As shown, snip off the two corners of the flat bottom that are folded in toward the open end of the bag.

2. Cut out the sign, at right, and glue on the bag, near the bottom (opening).

3. Cut out the alligator head pattern. Place it on a sheet of green construction paper (white paper will do; color green when done), allowing space along the dotted line side to turn it over and trace it again, as shown. This will give you a complete alligator's head.

4. Fold the eyes up. Fold the teeth down.

5. Glue the head onto the bag as shown, with the snout sticking out from the bottom of the bag. You can make the snout move with your fingers in the folded part of the bottom of the bag.

_____

IS A PLEASURE TO HAVE IN CLASS, BECAUSE

_____

_____

_____

_____

_____

Developing Good Citizens

- Teach the *Golden Rule* and refer to it often. Ask the children for examples and discuss. Can they explain what the Golden Rule will do for them?

- Make sure that your expectations of the children are not so high that they give up their quest to please you.

- Promote good citizenship with spontaneous rewards such as those in this section. Praise for even the smallest effort in this direction.

- Give children responsibilities in your classroom (care of plants, pets, chalkboard, etc.) and maintain charts or calendars for this purpose. Praise and reward children for handling their own tasks without reminders.

- Explore sibling relationships with your class. Do any of your students get along well with their brothers or sisters? If so, why? What can these children teach the rest of the class? Encourage them to share their ideas about why and how they enjoy their siblings.

- Another great topic to explore with your class is *authority*. When talking about who has authority and why, be sure to discuss all of the people in authority in the children's lives—teachers, parents, coaches, principals, instructors, baby-sitters, etc. Why is it important for someone to be the boss? What would happen to this class if the teacher left? Let them discover the answer for themselves through discussion.

Parent Pointers

Dear Parent(s),

From time to time I like to share ideas I find on helping you to help your child. This task of raising a youngster is a tough one. I'm sure you'll agree that most of us can use all the help we can get. I welcome your comments and ideas.

_____

Teacher/Date

General Parent Pointers

- Set a good example for your child. Remember that children learn what they live. You are their first and best teacher!

- Do not set your child up for failure. Make your expectations high, but fair and achievable.

- Rules should set reasonable boundaries, not fortresses.

- Be consistent and persistent with enforcing your family rules.

- Children must be taught to share. The best way to teach this is by example.

- Talk about and practice looking for ways to do random acts of kindness. Help your child be proud of these actions by praising lavishly.

- Children who are treated with respect will respect others.

- Children's self-respect will be tied to the meaningfulness of their activities. Their main job as kids is to get an education, but they should also contribute worthwhile help to the family. Age-appropriate chores allow a child to contribute to the running of his home and family. This will make him feel important and therefore build his self-respect.

Regarding Electronic Media

- As a parent, it is your right and responsibility to monitor and control your child's access to electronic media—TV, radio, computers, video games, internet surfing. All of these are powerful and must be monitored by you to assure that your child is benefiting. Multimedia learning can be a fun way to enhance your child's learning experiences, but remember that there is no substitute for daily active play.

- Multimedia's advantage over TV and movies is that it is not completely passive. Your child has to think and make decisions, selections, etc.

- When selecting multimedia programs for your child, keep in mind the educational opportunities. Even the most fun games to play can be educational. Kids enjoy a good challenge when presented in a fun atmosphere.

- Select CD-ROM programs which involve as much interaction as possible. Children should be given options, decision-making opportunities and challenges. These characteristics make learning fun, and CD-ROM graphics really bring it to life.

You've heard all the concern over our society becoming addicted to TV. Our kids spend more time watching TV than they do going to school. Setting family rules regarding TV viewing can no doubt demonstrate your priorities. Here are a few ideas.

- Chores and homework always come before TV.

- No TV on school nights.

- Replace TV time with other family activities—trip to the library, a family walk, park visit, an interactive CD-ROM game, a family card or board game.

- Videotape desirable shows which air at inappropriate times. View these later when time allows.

- A great way to limit TV and assure your kids get adequate exercise is to sign them up for sports, dance or other activities during the after school and evening hours. If they are left with just enough time for homework and chores, your goal is achieved. Look for activities for your child where grouped with kids your child's own age, and the social aspect will take care of itself, as well.

- If addiction is severe and unending, give up TV altogether! One of the authors' family did this five years ago and found it only took three days for the kids to adjust. Now, they are all more active, more physically fit and more successful in sports and school. (Note: There are those times when a TV is needed for important news or special events. We keep a small TV in the closet for just this purpose. It comes out for news, Olympic competitions, sports playoffs, finals and special events.

- Replace TV with video viewing only. This allows a great deal more control over content, timing and previewing.

Dear Parent(s),

This envelope of capital letters will give your child an opportunity to show off knowledge of the alphabet. You and your child will enjoy making this together, and it will be a great way to practice this very important skill. Remember to praise all efforts!

_____

Teacher/Date

Alphabet Envelope

Cut out these letters and insert them into the envelope you'll make from page 45.

I Know the Alphabet!

Dear Family,
Let me show you how I can name the letters of the alphabet. As you take the letters out of the envelope, I will name them for you.
Thanks!

A	B	C	D	E
F	G	H	I	J	K	L
M	N	O	P	Q	R	S
T	U	V	W	X	Y	Z

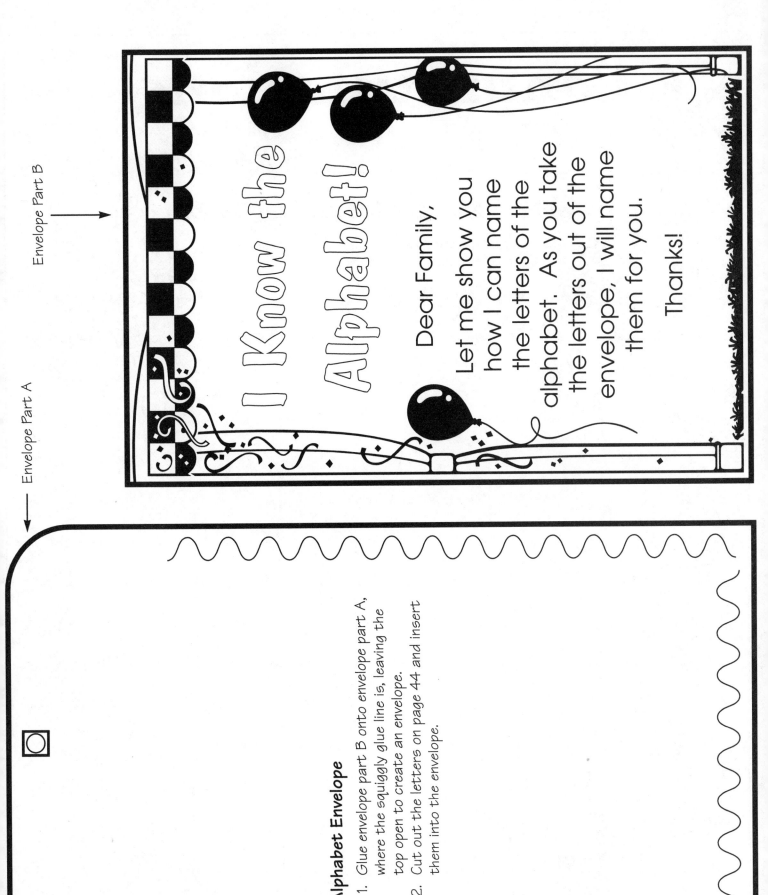

Envelope Part B →

Envelope Part A →

I Know the Alphabet!

Dear Family,

Let me show you how I can name the letters of the alphabet. As you take the letters out of the envelope, I will name them for you.

Thanks!

Alphabet Envelope

1. Glue envelope part B onto envelope part A, where the squiggly glue line is, leaving the top open to create an envelope.
2. Cut out the letters on page 44 and insert them into the envelope.

Congratulations,

_____, on Recognizing

Upper- and Lowercase Letters!

Match the upper- and lowercase letters.
The first one is done for you.

_____
Teacher/Date

Good Job!

_____

knows how to

write uppercase letters!

_____
Teacher/Date

Please demonstrate:

Hooray! _____ knows the
sounds of the letters!

Teacher/Date

Demonstrate by matching letters with a picture that starts with the same sound.

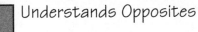

Announcing . . .

can write lowercase letters!

_____
Teacher/Date

Please write the lowercase letters beside the uppercase ones below.

A B C D E F G H I
J K L M N O P Q R
S T U V W X Y Z

Dear Parent(s),

Your child understands opposites. The exercise below gives a chance to demonstrate this knowledge for you. Be sure to give lots of praise.

_____
Teacher/Date

Match opposites.

dark	fun
big	tall
in	nice
short	light
boring	out
mean	small

Button or Necklace

1. Cut out and color.
2. Pin on, or . . .
3. Make a hole in the top and place string or yarn through to make a necklace.
4. Tie on and wear proudly!

I Can Name the DAYS of the WEEK! Ask Me!

Dear Parent(s),

Congratulations! Your child is doing well recognizing rhyming words. Below is an exercise to do at home. Have fun watching your child successfully complete this, and remember, your praise means more than anything!

_____

Teacher/Date

dog

more

dish

band

snake

tag

took

hut

Teacher/Date

Reads Aloud Well!

☑ Recognizes the Names of the Days of the Week   ☐ Can Name the Months of the Year   ☑ Recognizes the Months of the Year

Congratulations!

_____

recognizes the
**names of the
Days of the Week!**

Ask me:
Friday   Tuesday
Saturday   Sunday
Monday   Thursday
Wednesday

_____
Teacher/Date

Button or Necklace

1. Cut out and color.
2. Pin on, or . . .
3. Make a hole in the top and place string or yarn through to make a necklace.
4. Tie on and wear proudly!

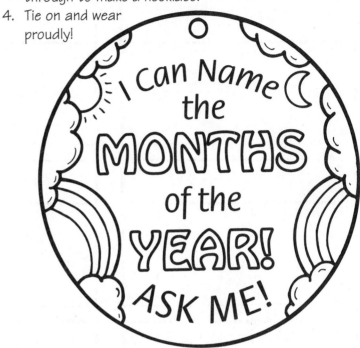

I Can Name the MONTHS of the YEAR! ASK ME!

Dear Parent(s),

Your child now recognizes the months of the year. This calendar activity is an award for this accomplishment. Please take a few minutes to help construct this simple calendar. It will give your child a place to remember special dates, such as birthdays and other family celebrations. This time spent with you will be an additional reward. Enjoy!

_____
Teacher/Date

Special Dates

Name _____

January	February	March

April	May	June

July	August	September

October	November	December

Calendar

1. Cut out the calendar on page 52 along the dotted lines.
2. Print your name on the line at the top in large letters.
3. Cut out the names of the months.
4. Glue the names of the months onto the calendar in the correct order.
5. Fill in any special dates to remember in the boxes. Don't forget your birthday!

Special Dates

Glue the month here.	Glue the month here.	Glue the month here.
Glue the month here.	Glue the month here.	Glue the month here.
Glue the month here.	Glue the month here.	Glue the month here.
Glue the month here.	Glue the month here.	Glue the month here.

January	February	March
April	May	June
July	August	September
October	November	December

Dear Parent(s),

Your child can now recognize the number words through 10. This simple puzzle is a reward for this accomplishment. Please help cut it out and glue it together onto a sheet of paper, like the sample on the right. As you work, have your child write in the numeral next to the written number. This special time spent with you will help to reinforce the learning. Remember to praise!

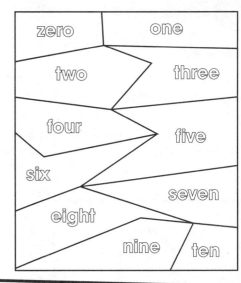

_____

Teacher/Date

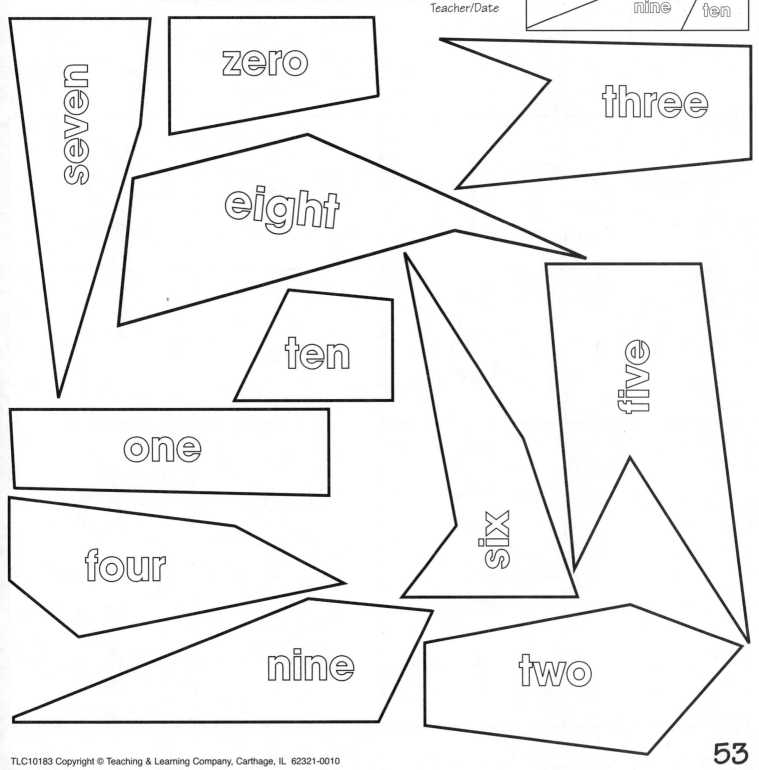

Dear Parent(s),

Below are cards for a game called Number Word Concentration. This is a reward for your child, who has now learned to recognize the number words up to 20. Remember to praise this accomplishment. Have fun playing this game.

_____
Teacher/Date

Number Word Concentration

1. Cut out all of the cards on the two sheets. You should have 42 cards, one for each number word from zero to twenty, and one for each numeral from 0 to 20.
2. Stack the cards so that all the number words and numbers are facing down, and shuffle the cards thoroughly.
3. Deal out all the cards facedown, using six rows, seven cards in each.
4. Players take turns turning over two cards, trying to find matches. (Ex: zero and 0)
5. If a match is turned up, the player keeps the matched cards and gets another turn. Play moves to another player when no match can be made.
6. When all cards are matched, the game ends. The player with the most matches is the winner.

0			
zero	1	one	2
two	3	three	4
four	5	five	6
six	7	seven	8

ten	13	fifteen	18	twenty
10	twelve	15	seventeen	20
nine	12	fourteen	17	nineteen
9	eleven	14	sixteen	19
eight	11	thirteen	16	eighteen

□ Knows All Sight Words ⊙

Dear Parent(s),

Congratulations! Your child has learned all the high frequency sight words. As a reward, I am sending home this reading wheel for you to make together. Enjoy this special time together. This wheel will be a fun way to practice this new skill. Have fun!

_____
Teacher/Date

Cut out.

56

Peek-a-Boo Reading Wheel

1. Cut out both wheels.
2. Cut out the word window as shown.
3. Color the wheel that has the window.
4. Using a brass fastener, attach the wheel with the window on top of the word wheel.
5. Turn the wheel to reveal words to read. Have fun practicing!

Teacher Tip

To extend this award as a better practice tool, make extra copies and hand write additional sight words onto the extras. These can be interchangeable.

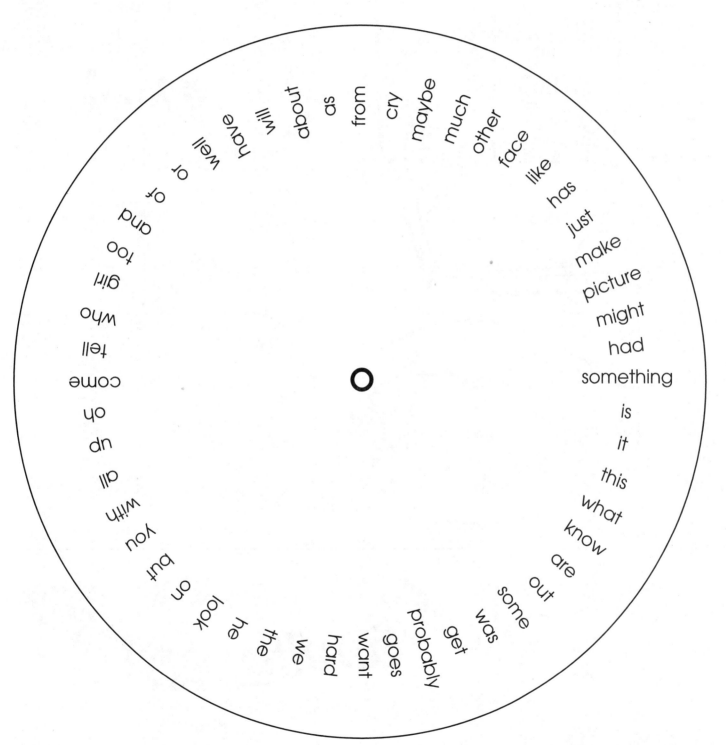

☐ Knows Name, Age and Telephone Number ☐ Spelling Bee Winner ☐ Can Retell a Story ☐ Great Speller Award

Button or Necklace

1. Cut out and color.
2. Pin on, or . . .
3. Make a hole in the top and place string or yarn through to make a necklace.
4. Tie on and wear proudly!

Ask ME!

I know my name, age and telephone number!

_____
Teacher/Date

Ribbon

1. Cut out and color the ribbon blue (for first place).
2. Pin on, or . . .
3. Place a string or yarn through a small hole to make a necklace.
4. Wear your award proudly.

You earned it!

Spelling BEE Winner

_____
Teacher/Date

Whoo

Can Retell a Story?

Can I

Teacher/Date

Goes to _____ !

GREAT Speller AWARD

_____
Teacher/Date

on your Book Report

For doing such a nice book report, you have earned this word search. Have fun!

_____
Teacher/Date

Words to Find

setting   problem   author   solution   fiction   nonfiction   title   characters

```
C  N  O  I  T  U  L  O  S  N
X  H  A  U  T  H  O  R  O  Z
M  O  A  L  S  V  E  N  J  G
E  G  H  R  A  C  F  V  L  N
L  V  K  N  A  I  P  B  V  I
B  R  Y  N  C  C  A  Z  T  T
O  C  L  T  C  S  T  Y  K  T
R  D  I  G  G  Z  E  E  N  E
P  O  T  I  T  L  E  S  R  S
N  G  N  O  I  T  C  I  F  S
```

Answer key on page 62.

_____ Knows Our Vocabulary WORDS!

Please ask for a demonstration of the words below.

_____
Teacher/Date

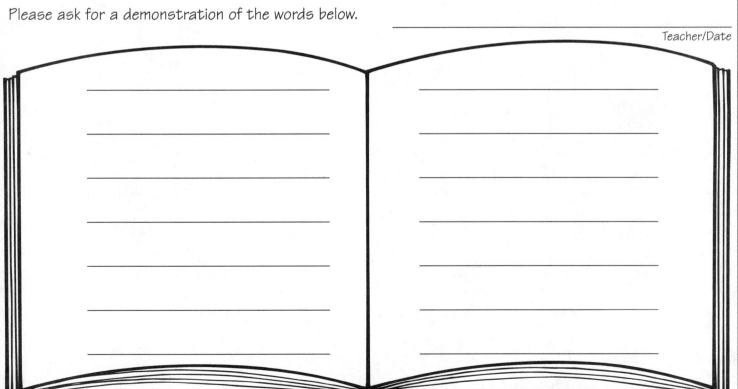

BRAVO!

I can name each of these **punctuation marks** and use them in a sentence!

Ask for this demonstration. Name each of these punctuation marks and tell where each is used:

. ? ! ,

_____
Teacher/Date

Pencil Topper

1. Color and cut out.
2. Neatly print your name on the line.
3. Cut the slits as shown.
4. Slide the topper over the top of your pencil to display your award.

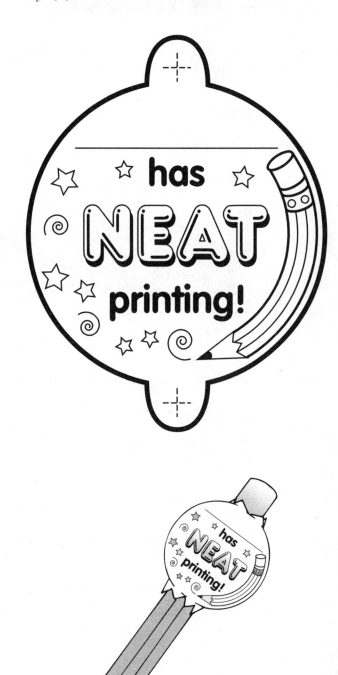

_____ has NEAT printing!

Language Arts Teacher Tips

- Take a related field trip to introduce a new unit.
- Invite guest speakers, older students or parents to share their favorite stories.
- Listen to the beginning of a story on cassette tape.
- To spark interest, bring in objects related to the story.
- Have the children dress as a character in the story and share a summary of it.
- As an ending activity, cook something from the story or have children bring in samples of food from the story.
- Have a book swap. Each child can donate a book.

Motivate Your Students to Read By . . .

- Having children keep track of the number of hours read at home. A sample form and letter to go home are on page 63.
- Rewarding them with a certificate, sticker or random drawing for a prize donated by a local merchant. (Ex: free French fries or ice cream cone)
- Having a reading corner in your room. Make it a fun place to go, with pillows, beanbag chairs or a rocking chair where the children can escape with good books.
- Reading aloud from a high-interest book each day. Have the children predict what will happen today and summarize what happened yesterday, before reading.

After Reading a Story

- Write a newspaper article about a major event from the book.
- Write a letter to a main character from the book, giving advice or solving the problem.
- Create finger puppets or paper bag puppets of the main characters. Have a play to re-create events from the story.
- Make a time line of important events from the story.

Developing Young Writers' Skills

- Allow your students to choose their own topics for writing as often as possible.
- A great way to develop writing skills is daily journal writing. This can be done first thing in the morning or just before leaving school, depending on the type of journal used.

Types of Journals

1. **Diary or Feelings Journal:** This is the child's personal record.
2. **Response Journal:** This journal is used for responding to books they have read, TV shows viewed, movies seen or any other activity you may suggest.
3. **Learning Log:** This journal is a place for the child to keep track of what he has learned.

Try to collect, read and respond to the journals every few days. Students love to read your feedback and receive your praise.

Teacher Tips

- Younger children may "write" stories with pictures at first, then progress to a word or two along with the picture. Let them use invented spelling in their early stage. Sentences, and eventually paragraphs, will follow.

- By third grade students should begin using a dictionary and/or an electronic speller to recognize and correct their own errors.

- Allow your students to begin a new story, even if they haven't completed a previous one. When they are ready, they'll go back to the first one.

- Have the students date their work each day. This will help monitor their progress.

- Allow the children to "publish" their completed stories. Set up a parent-run Classroom Publishing Company. Parents can type (or help the child type) the stories on the computer. The stories can then be illustrated by the child, along with an "About the Author" page, and the story can become a book by using a book-binding machine. If your school doesn't have a binding machine, construction paper; cloth samples; clear, self-adhesive paper or wallpaper samples make great covers, too. Allow the children to share their new books with classmates and add to your classroom library.

- Develop good writing habits by teaching the five stages in the writing process: prewriting, writing, revising, editing, proofreading and finally, publishing.

Answer Key

Good Job on Your Book Report! p. 59

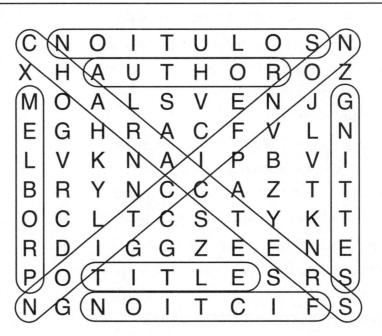

TLC10183 Copyright © Teaching & Learning Company, Carthage, IL 62321-0010

Dear Parent(s),

A Home Reading Log is a tool to help your child develop good reading habits. It will count as part of your child's reading grade. Based on your child's reading ability at this time, I have set a goal of _____ per week for your child's reading time.

Please help your child fill out the log each day. At the end of the week, you can assist with totaling the time read during the week, and then sign the bottom. Please make sure that the form is in your child's backpack to go to school on Friday.

Any reading material is acceptable: books, textbooks, magazines, newspapers and even comic books. The goal is to hook your child on reading, so encourage reading whatever your child enjoys.

A timer works well to help keep track of the time read. If finding time is difficult, allow your child to read anywhere and everywhere you go.

I encourage you to set a good example for your young reader. If reading is an important part of your life, it will become an important part of your child's life.

Happy Reading!

_____
Teacher/Date

Helpful Tips for Students

You will be given a Home Reading Log each Friday. It is to be turned in the following Friday. You are responsible for getting it signed and brought to school each week.

1. To make sure you do not forget your Home Reading Log on Friday, put it in your book bag or backpack on Thursday night, after filling it out.

2. Keep your Home Reading Log in a place where you will see it easily. (Ex: refrigerator, bulletin board, desk, bedroom door)

3. Read at least _____ per week. The more time you can read, the better. It may take a little help from Mom or Dad to schedule it into your day.

4. Keep track of the time you read each day. Write it down the same day, so you do not forget.

5. You, not your parents, are responsible for bringing the Home Reading Log to school on time. Write yourself a note in your assignment notebook or planner to help you remember.

Home Reading Log

Name _____

Day	# Minutes Read	Title of Book/Material
Friday		
Saturday		
Sunday		
Monday		
Tuesday		
Wednesday		
Thursday		
Total Time Read		

Parent's Signature _____

Parent Pointers

Dear Parent(s),

Fostering a love of reading will do more to ensure a good education than anything else a parent can do. Attached are a few ideas that you might enjoy incorporating into your activities with your child. Let me know how you like these ideas, and feel free to pass along any ideas you have as well. Thank you!

_____

Teacher/Date

Developing Reading Skills

- Read daily to your child. Reading equals quality time. Being read to helps young prereaders develop a sense of the patterning that occurs in sentences.

- Once your child begins to read, listen to your child read daily, even if only a few sentences.

- Set aside a special reading time each day for your child to "drop everything and read!" Set a good example; you can read, too!

- After reading, have your child retell the story to you. Help sequence events from the story. Use the illustrations from the book to help with this.

- Ask your child about the characters, setting, plot and ending of each story after you finish reading.

- Have your child rate the book read (1-10). Ask why that rating.

Helping Your Child Become a Reader

- Have books on your child's level available to read.

- Give books as gifts.

- Visit the library often to get books on your child's interests. Encourage your child to select different types of literature for varied exposure.

- Read aloud to your child regularly.

- Give short "commercials" on books you plan to read in the coming days—hook your kid.

- Allow your child to choose the book to read.

- Take your child to the library to get a personal library card. This will be a joyful possession.

- Praise all your child's efforts at reading (even the alphabet or wordless books), writing and listening to others read.

- As a prereader, let your child try out some wordless books. Your child can "read" them to you.

- Have a reading sleep-over. Ask your friend(s) to bring some books to share.

- Set an example by reading regularly.

- Associate reading with pleasure. Never make it seem like a chore.

When Reading Aloud to Your Child

- Set aside time for reading aloud that is free from distractions—especially TV.

- Allow your child to make choices about what to read.

- Read with expression and change your voice to fit the characters you are reading about.
- Talk about the pictures. Use them to have your child retell the story to you.
- Encourage your child to ask questions about the story.
- Ask your child questions about what you are reading. (Ex: What was your child's favorite part? Funniest part? Saddest part? How did the story end?) Rate the book 1-10.
- Before reading, ask your child to predict what the story will be about. Later, ask your child to predict what will happen next or how the story will end.
- After reading, help your child act out the story or a scene from the story.

When Listening to Your Child Read to You

- Always be upbeat and positive about your child's choice of book.
- Discuss the cover. Skim through to look at the pictures and ask your child to make predictions.
- Help with unfamiliar words by having your child read the rest of the sentence and then try to figure out the word from context. Encourage trying to sound out the word. If these two methods do not work, give a clue to the meaning or pronounce the word.

Inexpensive Ways to Obtain Books/Reading Materials

- Classroom, school or public library
- Swap books with friends
- School book fairs
- Classroom book orders (book clubs)
- Local, state or federally funded programs like RIF (Reading Is Fundamental)

- Subscribe to newspapers and magazines
- Garage sales and used bookstores

Developing Your Child's Writing Skills

- Provide your child with lots of opportunities to write, such as grocery lists, letters and thank-you notes.
- Have your child keep a journal. In the beginning stages of writing, have your child express thoughts with a picture. As your child progresses, add a word, then a sentence, then a paragraph to the picture. A spiral notebook works well and keeps writing sequential. Remember to date each entry.

Types of Journals

1. **Diary:** Have your child keep a personal record of daily events.
2. **Response Journal:** Have your child respond to books, movies and TV shows.
3. **Learning Log:** Have your child write about what was learned at school each day.

- Have a special time and a special place to write. Try to have your child write every day.
- Keep a file of pictures from magazines and newspapers to use as story starters on a rainy day.
- Brainstorm topics for stories with your child. Keep a running list in a file.
- Help your child "publish" writings in a home-made book.
- Look for computer software programs that help with writing skills.

☐ Recognizes Numbers 1 to 10 ▨ Knows Addition Facts to 20 ▨ Recognizes Coins by Name

Dear Parent(s),

Please congratulate your child for recognizing the numbers 1 to 10. As a special reward for learning this new skill, I am sending home this number necklace craft for you to make with your child. This special time together will further reward your child for this accomplishment. Have fun!

_____
Teacher/Date

Number Necklace

1. Cut out the numbers and color each a different color, if possible.

2. Put a hole punch in the top of each number.

3. Thread a piece of yarn or string through all the holes to make a necklace.

4. Tie on and wear with pride. Have fun demonstrating your new skill.

1	2	3	4	5
6	7	8	9	10

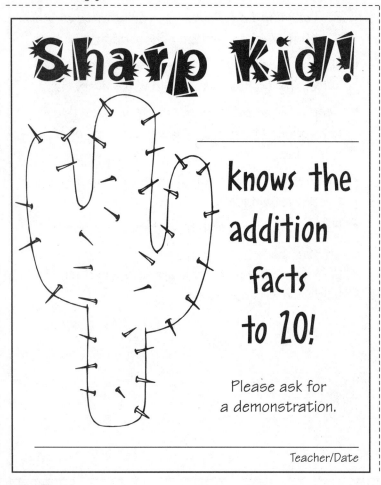

Sharp Kid!

_____

knows the addition facts to 20!

Please ask for a demonstration.

_____
Teacher/Date

I Can Sort Coins by name!

Please let me sort yours!

_____
Teacher/Date

66

Dear Parent(s),

Your child has earned this paper bag puppet for learning to count to 10. Please help create this cute pirate to boast this new skill. Have fun!

_____

Teacher/Date

Paper Bag Puppet

1. Cut out and color the pirate's bandana, beard, eye patch and sign.
2. Glue each part onto the paper bag as shown.
3. Draw on the remaining facial features.
4. Have fun telling everyone your good news! Ahoy, Matey!

Beard

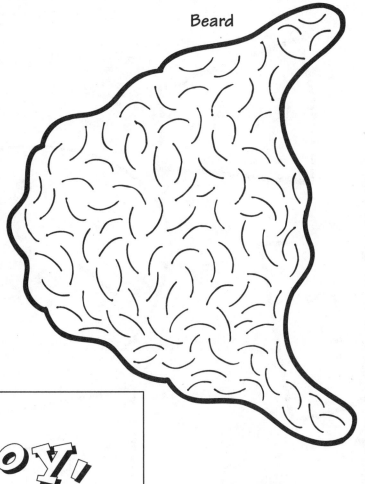

Bandana

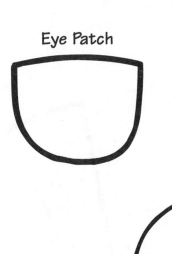

Eye Patch

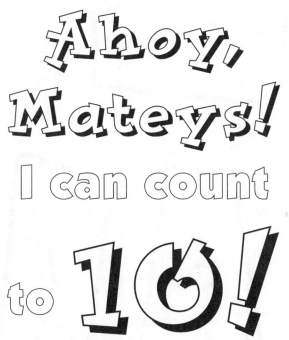

Ahoy, Mateys! I can count to 10!

Dear Parent(s),

Your child can count to 20. Please celebrate by creating this snake craft. This will be fun for both of you and will provide extra reinforcement of this new skill. Enjoy!

_____
Teacher/Date

Snake Puzzle

1. Cut out the snake parts below.
2. Glue together in number order on a piece of plain white or colored paper, as shown above.
3. Color the numbered sections in a pattern (Ex: 2 reds, 1 blue) of your choice to make a colorful snake.
4. Have fun practicing your counting with your new friend!

I can count to 100

Watch Me!

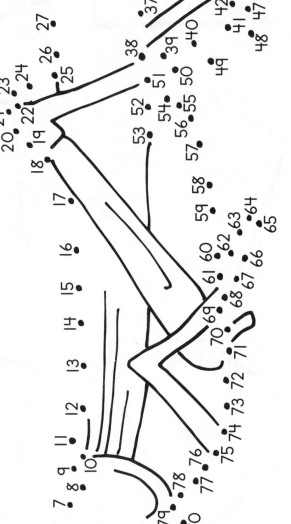

Teacher/Date

Connect the dots to finish the picture.

We Are Members of the Number 10 Club

☐ Knows Addition Facts to 10   ☐ Knows Addition with Carrying/Regrouping

Teacher Tips

Using the wall chart on page 71, immediately pay tribute to a child's completion of the goal by placing name on the chart in large, bold letters. The bookmark is a personal reward for this skill, which the child may take home, color and show off to parents.

Along the way to this goal, be sure to openly praise children who are coming close; this personal attention may be all that is needed to get over this hump. Perhaps the children who have reached the goal would enjoy holding flash cards or helping those who are struggling a bit. This, too, is a reward for the children who have completed the goal. Being a teacher's helper is often a special treat for primary children, as you know. Use this power whenever you can.

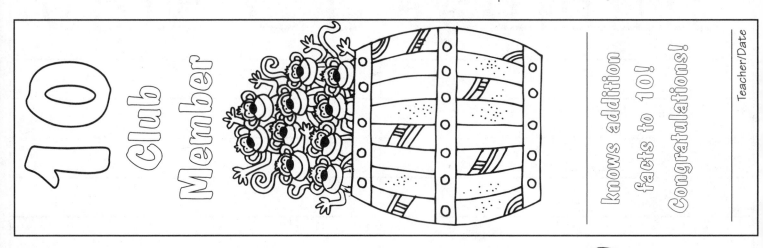

Dear Parent(s),

Your child has mastered the skill of addition with carrying. This craft is a reward for this accomplishment. Please help make this finger puppet. Remember that your praise and this time spent with you are the best rewards of all.

_____
Teacher/Date

Finger Puppet

1. Cut out and color the scarecrow.
2. Cut strips of paper for finger loops.
3. Tape loops to the back of the scarecrow's arms. Use your thumb and pointer finger in these loops to make the scarecrow's arms move.
4. Have fun singing farm songs with your scarecrow: "The Farmer in the Dell," "Old MacDonald Had a Farm," etc.

72

I Know Subtraction Facts to 10!

_____
Teacher/Date

Here is a demonstration.

9	4	6	5	3	8	10
− 8	− 2	− 3	− 0	− 3	− 7	− 5

7	10	1	9	2	5	3
− 5	− 7	− 0	− 6	− 1	− 2	− 1

Answer key on page 80.

Color by number: 1 = red, 2 = blue, 3 = green

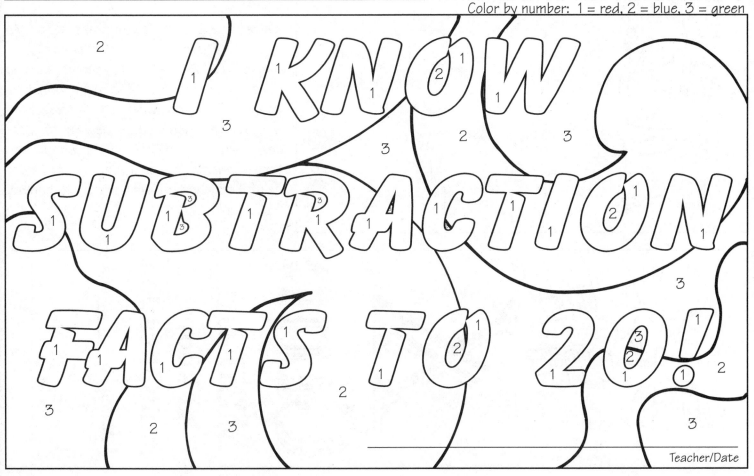

_____
Teacher/Date

BRAVO!

_____

knows subtraction with regrouping!

_____

Teacher/Date

Watch me demonstrate my new skill. I can do the problems on the award.

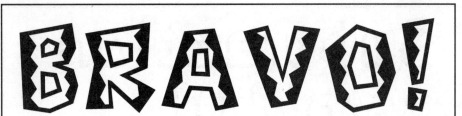

17	28	56
− 8	− 9	− 7
☐	☐	☐

36	42	12
− 8	− 14	− 9
☐	☐	☐

84	60	70
− 65	− 16	− 23
☐	☐	☐

Answer key on page 80.

Teacher Tips

As you know, mastering the multiplication tables is a critical life skill. As such, it deserves greater attention than most math skills, to obtain the needed energy, effort and enthusiasm from your students. Place a colorful copy of the chart on page 75 on your wall, with each child's name listed in alphabetical order. As the child masters the multiplication facts for each number (1-10), the corresponding square can be stickered, stamped or initialed.

At any point along the way, when you note the beginning of a frustration, use the bookmark to reward the facts the child has learned so far. This may be just enough of a lift to keep the child going. If you need more intermediate awards, try giving out magic triangles or magic squares to take home. Offer a sticker or other prize to return this fun math challenge.

We recommend that you make a sample of the final award (the mobile to make, on pages 76-77) as a statement of the reward to come. You also might consider throwing a party when the whole class achieves an acceptable degree of success, an offer which could encourage those ahead in the game to be more helpful to the kids who are a bit behind. Good luck!

X Club Member
I know multiplication facts to ____!

Teacher/Date

Knows Multiplication Facts to 10

X CLUB

Name	0	1	2	3	4	5	6	7	8	9	10

Dear Parent(s),

Your child has successfully learned the multiplication tables. This is an essential skill for life and deserves much praise. I am rewarding this accomplishment with a mobile to make at home. I hope you will enjoy making this together.

_____

Teacher/Date

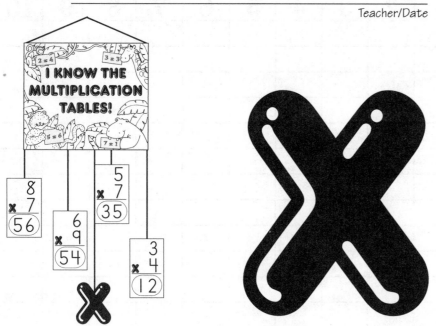

Multiplication Mobile

1. Copy this page and the header on the next page onto colored card stock.

2. Cut out the four rectangular cards shown here.

3. Using the cards, prepare flash cards with multiplication problems as shown at left.

4. Tie a piece of yarn or string about 22" (56 cm) long through the center of another piece of card stock. Tape the string to the paper. Put a loop at the top for hanging. Reinforce the hole with tape.

5. Tape the header sheet to the string, beginning about 3" (8 cm) down.

6. Tape the X symbol to the bottom of the string, which hangs well below the header.

7. Tape strings 11" to 16" (28 to 41 cm) long to each corner of the card stock on top.

8. Tape the flash cards to the ends of the four strings and hang to enjoy.

I KNOW THE MULTIPLICATION TABLES!

☑ Counts Money (coins/bills) ☐ Can Solve Word Problems ☐ Can Add ___-Digit Numbers ☑ Can Tell Time

THIS IS A HOLDUP ...

Hold up all your money and let me count it!

I can count money—coins and bills. Please let me demonstrate.

Teacher/Date

Pencil Topper

1. Cut out and color.

Can Solve WORD Problems

2. Cut small slits where shown.

3. Proudly display your award on your pencil.

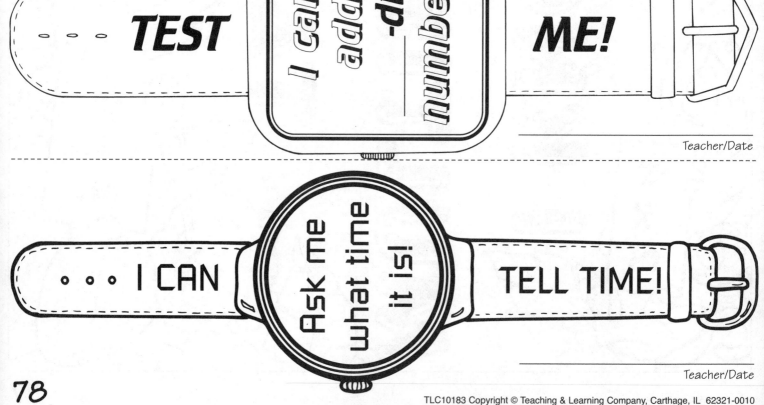

· · · TEST

I can add ___-digit numbers!

ME!

Teacher/Date

· · · I CAN

Ask me what time it is!

TELL TIME!

Teacher/Date

Button or Necklace

1. Cut out and color.
2. Pin on, or . . .
3. Make a hole in the top and place string or yarn through to make a necklace.
4. Tie on and wear proudly!

Dear Parent(s),

Do you know the difference between < and > ?
I do! Just watch me.

Circle the correct statements.

14 < 60   43 > 67

39 > 12   56 < 39

27 < 65   19 > 6

14 > 15   46 < 51

Answer key on page 80.   Teacher/Date

Leapin' Lizards!
I Know Odd and Even Numbers!

Color odd numbers green.
Color even numbers brown.

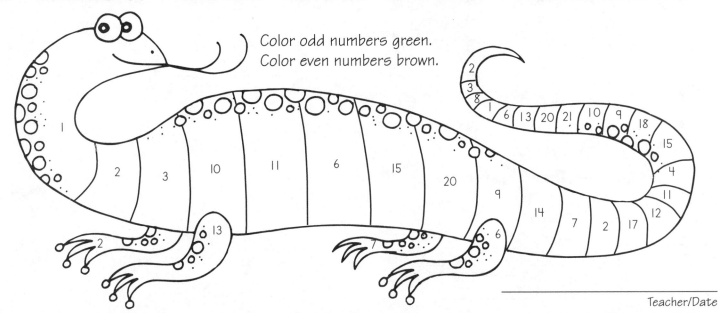

Teacher/Date

Teacher Tips

- You can help your students connect math to the real world through career days. Invite speakers to talk about how they use math in their jobs.

- Encourage your students to use mental math regularly. Practice will help them gain confidence.

- Plot a course for a class field trip and figure the distance. Estimate how long it will take to get there.

- Use classifying and graphing to analyze information from a field trip. Ex: How many species of reptiles did we see at the zoo? What about rodents, birds, mammals, etc?

- Manipulatives make math fun and real. Use blocks, scales, counters and sorters, clocks, measuring tools, money, etc., in the classroom.

- Explore an atlas; discover populations, travel distances, etc.

- Measure, measure, measure. The more students measure, the better they will estimate.

Test phobias begin in the primary grades. You can help prevent some of this by teaching good test-taking strategies to your students now.

- Relax and take a deep breath before you start.

- Read all the directions carefully before you start. Remember that missing even one word can affect your understanding of the instructions. Don't skim.

- Ask about anything you don't completely understand in the instructions.

- Carefully study all graphs, tables and pictures that are referred to in the problem.

- Skip problems you don't understand. Go back to them at the end, if you have time.

- When appropriate, draw a picture or diagram to help find the solution.

- Check your work. Is the answer reasonable? Did you answer every part of the question? If required to show your work, did you include every step in your answer?

Answer Key

Knows Subtraction Facts to 10, p. 73

9	4	6	5	3	8	10
− 8	− 2	− 3	− 0	− 3	− 7	− 5
1	2	3	5	0	1	5

7	10	1	9	2	5	3
− 5	− 7	− 0	− 6	− 1	− 2	− 1
2	3	1	3	1	3	2

Understands Less Than/Greater Than, p. 79

(14 < 60)	43 > 67		
(39 > 12)	56 < 39		
(27 < 65)	(19 > 6)		
14 > 15	(46 < 51)		

Knows Subtraction with Regrouping/Borrowing, p. 74

17	28	56
− 8	− 9	− 7
9	19	49

36	42	12
− 8	− 14	− 9
28	28	3

84	60	70
− 65	− 16	− 23
19	44	47

80

Dear Parent(s),

Moms and dads often ask me for ideas to help them develop their child's math skills or to get him or her more interested in math. Try some of these, and please, let me know how they worked with your child.

Teacher/Date

Helping Your Child Connect Math to the Real World

On Family Errands

- Encourage your child to ask questions of anyone whose job involves math: the bank teller, grocery cashier, carpenters . . . nearly everyone uses math in some way in their job.

- Help your child comparison shop for an item your child wishes to purchase.

- Take the city bus. Explore routes, schedules, costs and time factors. Compare each to travel in the car.

- Before you check out, encourage your child to use "mental math" or estimation to predict how much you have spent.

While Shopping for and Preparing Foods

- Discuss how much food is needed to serve your family.

- When using coupons, have your child calculate the cost, after deducting the discount.

- Let your child help you make dinner. Let your child read the recipe and measure the ingredients.

- Double a recipe for something you are cooking or baking together. While discussing the measurement changes, point out the challenge a restaurant cook or baker must have when making a recipe for dozens of people.

Using Resources You Have at Home to Connect Math to the Real World

- Plant a garden—plan for space, vegetable choices, amount of seeds needed, watering and weeding schedules, growth time, harvest schedule.

- Encourage your child to explore with a calculator.

- Go window shopping on the internet. How much does it cost to get your favorite item shipped to you?

- Explore the toolbox and compare sizes of wrenches.

- Look for patterns in fabrics, wallpaper, wrapping paper, music and dance.

- Manipulatives make math fun and real: blocks, scales, counting and sorting things, clocks, measuring tools, money, etc.

- Measure, measure, measure. Show your child how to use a ruler, yardstick and tape measure. The more he measures, the better he will estimate.

- Purchase software for your home computer that allows basic skills to be reviewed and practiced in a fun way.

AWWK!

Thanks for being a good listener in science!

Teacher/Date

Dear Parent(s),

Your child has had very good participation in science class. To encourage continuing with this great behavior, I am sending home an activity for you to do together. Let your child know how important you find participation in science. This time that you spend with your child will be very special and will be an added part of this reward. Thanks and have fun!

_____
Teacher/Date

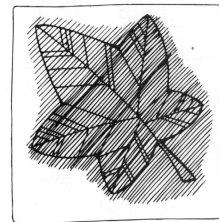

Textured Rubbings

Making rubbings is a fun way to explore the many textures of things around us.

1. First, select several items that have texture from around your home and yard. Good choices are coins, leaves, award plaques, screen, wallpaper, burlap or other textured cloth—even an automobile license plate.
2. Place a piece of plain paper over the textured area. Hold it securely in place with one hand. Holding a pencil or crayon almost flat, as shown, color back and forth quickly over the item, covering all of the textured area.
3. Your texture, design or engraving will appear on your paper. Often you will notice that the texture is more noticeable in your rubbing, allowing you to study it more carefully.

Badge or Necklace

1. Cut out and color.
2. Pin on, or . . .
3. Make a hole in the top and place string or yarn through to make a necklace.
4. Tie on and wear proudly!

Color and cut out.

Follows Class Rules in SCIENCE!

Teacher/Date

Cut along dotted lines. Color and hang up.

A **SUPER** **Scientist** lives here!

Teacher/Date

Dear Parent(s),

To reward your child for following directions so well in science class, I am sending home a Chinese tangram puzzle. You and your child can have fun together reassembling the parts of this puzzle to make objects. After you cut the pieces below apart, try making some of the objects shown, or make up a few of your own.

This special time spent with your child will be an added reinforcement to this reward. I hope you both enjoy this challenging, creative activity.

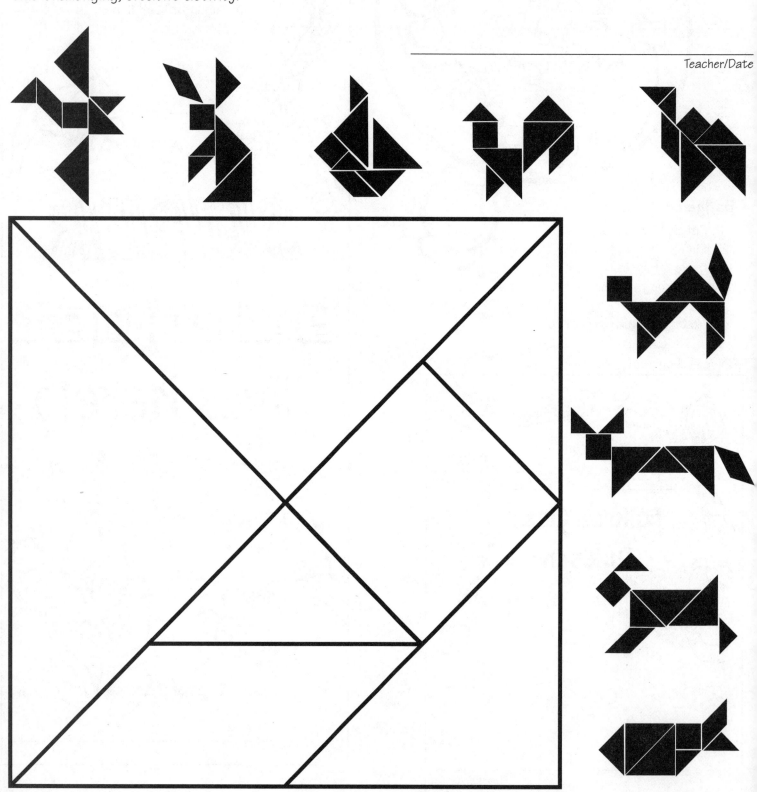

Teacher/Date

Dear Parent(s),

Your child's understanding of maps and globes is beginning to blossom. To reward these new skills and encourage continued interest, I am sending home this necklace to make. I hope you enjoy making this project with your child.

_____
Teacher/Date

N ____

W _____ E _____

S ____

I Understand MAPS and GLOBES

_____
Teacher/Date

Demonstration Necklace

1. On the globe at the right, label the North Pole, South Pole and equator.

2. Using N, S, E and W, label north, south, east and west on the direction key above.

3. Color and cut out the two parts of the necklace.

4. Glue them together to make one necklace, with a back and a front.

5. Punch a hole in the top.

6. Tie a piece of yarn or string through the hole to make a necklace.

Teacher Tips

Basic Rules for Science Experiments in Class

- Do not ever taste anything unless the teacher tells you it is safe!

- Whenever a child wishes to smell an unknown substance, wave the smell toward the nose or fan it.

- Plan ahead for controlled movement of children and materials to lessen the chance for spills, etc.

- Use safety goggles whenever liquid is being poured. A lab jacket to protect clothing is advisable.

- Keep hands away from eyes and mouth during lab work.

- Do not mix any chemicals or materials without permission.

Simple Science Explorations

- Have your class make a weather chart including temperature, rain, wind, clouds and other forms of precipitation.

- Use shadow play as a reward for good class behavior. They will love having the lights out and making hand puppets on the wall. Try a silhouette play in the dark.

- Explore how plants drink. The old standby experiment with carnations in colored water is still a hit with the kids. Don't forget to snip the ends before placing them in the water.

- Fascinate your kids with this question: How many times can you fold a piece of paper in half? No more than about nine. Why? The paper becomes too thick to fold.

- Do some magnifying glass exploration around your playground or classroom.

- Observing ants is fascinating. Even young children will be able to learn much about them, simply by watching them interact and travel. A classroom ant farm can enhance this value by allowing the children to watch as the pathways change from week to week.

- Grow some flowers from seeds. Also, try growing a plant from a vegetable seed; avocados work well. Place a few toothpicks around the middle and place the avocado in a heavy glass full of water. Place it in the sun, keep it full of water, and soon you will have an avocado plant.

- Visit nearby science and hands-on museums, planetariums, zoos, bird sanctuaries and other nature areas.

- Split into groups and ask each to invent a new machine. Draw and describe what it does.

- Collect and save maps, atlases and globes—old and new. Make these available to your children to explore regularly. Many maps are available through the internet—a rich source of geographical information.

Dear Parent(s),

Fostering curiosity and a love of learning about new things is the basis for interest in science. With this note I am attaching a few ideas to help you get started with expanding your child's interest in the world around him. Remember not to get bogged down with too much detail when exploring. Keeping it spontaneous and fun will make it seem less like learning and more like play. Have fun!

_____

Teacher/Date

- Use your free weekends and summers to plan interesting trips and outings to new places. Try a storytelling festival, museums, parks, unusual towns, festivals of all types, gardens, community events and sports competitions.

- How many times can you fold a piece of paper in half? Until you try it, you'll probably think it can be folded many more times, but actually only about nine. Why? The paper becomes too thick to bend.

- Magnifying glass exploration is a joy for children, especially if you can help them find interesting things to view. Try out your pet, too!

- Look for examples of pollution and discuss their sources.

- Discuss the three forms of matter (liquid, solid and gas) and help your child find examples.

- Make a family tree. Talk about relatives and help her begin to understand the relationships.

- Remember carnations in colored water? This is still a fantastic science experience to teach kids how plants drink. Don't forget to snip the ends of the carnation before placing them in the water.

- What path does food take through your body? Does your child know where digestion begins and the path it takes through the body?

- Colds and flu come from viruses which we come in contact with. Discuss what you can do to limit your chances of catching one.

- Create a homemade weather chart including temperature, precipitation, wind and clouds.

- Shadow play is great fun. In a dark room, place a light on one side of the room, pointing toward the other side. Try some shadow puppetry with your hands.

- When you visit the ocean, be sure to expose your child to the change in tides.

- Talk about the water cycle. Where do the puddles on the street go after the rain?

- Go cloud watching. Can you find cirrus (high and feathery), stratus (low and smooth), cumulus (large and fluffy) and cumulonimbus clouds (thunderstorm clouds)?

- Explore a space book or map to discover the planets of our solar system and their location with regard to Earth. Enjoy some star-gazing on a clear night. A sky map at the library will make this even more fun.

Parent Pointers

- Discuss how the sun and stars are the same. Why do the stars appear so small?

- Visit a planetarium for more fun and exploration.

- Explore a U.S. map for major points—large mountain ranges, the Great Lakes, major rivers and cities and the oceans and countries which form the borders.

- A U.S. map puzzle with each piece being a state is a fun and educational gift. This fun activity will help your child begin to learn the locations of the states and their capitals.

- Practice naming the continents using different globes and maps.

- Take a walk with a compass and learn how it is used. Why does it always point north?

- Discuss temperature. What temperature is comfortable at home? At what temperature does water freeze? When does water boil? Practice reading a thermometer.

- Talk about gravity. Test it by dropping various objects. Amazing! They all fall down!

- Collect some magnets of various sizes and shapes. Explore their reactions to one another and have fun seeing which stick and which repel.

- The lessons learned from balancing items on a scale will go with your child always.

TLC10183 Copyright © Teaching & Learning Company, Carthage, IL 62321-0010

Teacher Tips

Attach a copy of the chart header below to a copy of the chart grid on page 128. Trim off all but one or two of the rows of squares, to make the reward more attainable. Each day that the class has a generally cooperative day, as a group, award them with a sticker, stamp or your initials in one box on the grid.

Free time in art class is often the ultimate reward, as many primary children love to draw without any rules. Let them pick their own topic, but help them get started with a few ideas. Put a list on the board on award day, and give them a few choices of medium, as well. Perhaps oil pastels, colored pencils, chalk on dark paper, whatever variety is readily available. It will make the children feel really special to be given a choice. Once this award has been earned, the children will work even harder to earn it again.

Class Name

You Get an E for Effort in Art Class!

Enjoy this word search as your reward!

Words to Find

art
clay
color
crafts
create
cut
draw
glue
paint
sculpture

```
S Z V C U S A D W P
Y C J A T R D T N W
J M U F T N U M H B
D R A L C S G M K W
J R I H P R K S R A
C O U B J T E T Y R
G L U E W I U A U D
N O X Y A L C R T C
P A I N T S U W E E
C O L O R N N A U H
```

Answer key on page 93.

Teacher/Date

89

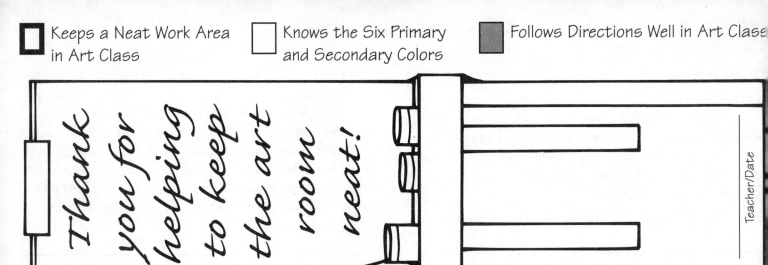

Thank you for helping to keep the art room neat!

Teacher/Date

I Know the 6 Primary and Secondary Colors!

Color in the paints with the six primary and secondary colors.

Teacher/Date

Dear Parent(s),

For following directions well in art class, your child is receiving this home activity as a reward. I hope you enjoy this craft with your child.

Teacher/Date

Flying Fish

1. Cut a 1" (2.5 cm) strip off the top of a piece of paper.

2. Cut two slits as shown here.

3. Bring the two ends together and slide the slits into each other.

4. Hold the flounder up by the tail and drop for a flurrying flight.

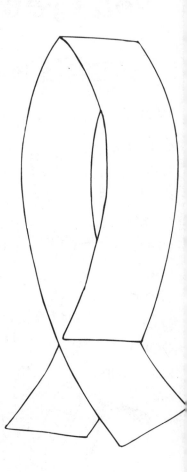

Cut along dotted lines.
Color and hang up.

CREATIVE ARTIST

Lives Here!

Teacher/Date

I Know the Color Words! Ask Me!

yellow

orange

green

red

blue

purple

Color in the paints with the correct colors.

Teacher/Date

Dear Parent(s),

As an award for your enthusiastic artist, I am sending home a craft for you to do together. All you need are scissors, glue and a toilet paper roll to create this cute reward that can be displayed on a desk or dresser. Have fun!

_____
                                    Teacher/Date

Panda

1. Cut out the panda patterns provided. Use the paw pattern to make three more paws.
2. Glue the panda's body on the toilet paper tube.
3. Glue the feet at the bottom of the tube (tabs inside at the front of the tube).
4. Fold the tabs of the paws and glue to the sides of the tube to complete the panda.

- -

Dear Parent(s),

Your child is receiving this art award for _____.
This wind sock to make will be a fun activity for you to do together.
Enjoy this time with your special child!

_____
                                    Teacher/Date

Supplies

disposable paper or plastic cup, or small ice cream container
crepe paper, about 12' (3.6 m)
yarn or string
glue and scissors

Wind Sock

1. Cut the bottom out of the cup or ice cream container.
2. Glue crepe paper around the cup, as shown, to cover the cup.
3. Cut several strips of crepe paper, each about 2' (.61 m) long.
4. Glue strips onto the inside of the cup and allow to dry.
5. Staple and tape a 1' to 2' (.30 to .61 m) piece of yarn or string to both sides of the top for a hanging loop.
6. Hang inside by an open window.

92

Motivating Young Artists

- Children love doing. Allow your students the opportunity to experiment with all available mediums. Encourage imagination and enthusiasm.

- Display artwork in the cafeteria, principal's conference room, media center and the office. The children feel a sense of pride when they see their creations, and parents love it, too!

- In conjunction with a PTA meeting (or anytime you are able), have an Art Open House. Display artwork of **all** the students throughout the hallways. Be available to parents to describe your program.

- Have a featured "Artist(s) of the Week" bulletin board. Display the artwork in a prominent place for all to see. Take it another step and have a Faculty/Staff Artist of the week, too. Everyone will enjoy seeing the talent of the school faculty and staff.

- Feature your students' designs and creations at local arts and crafts shows. Give certificates to featured artists, announce their names on the intercom and include mention of this honor in the school newsletter.

- When displaying student artwork, always include the child's name, grade and teacher's name. You might add a special "art plate" to each creation with this information on it.

- Use the internet to find answers to art trivia questions. Have a new question each week.

- Use volunteers to plan programs about famous artists. A 15-minute presentation could include samples of the artist's works and information about his life. The volunteer might even enjoy dressing or acting like the artist, to spice up the presentation a bit.

- Offer an occasional group project such as mural painting as a cooperative learning exercise.

- Encourage classroom teachers to include art museums in their field trip plans.

Answer Key

Extra Effort in Art Class, p. 89

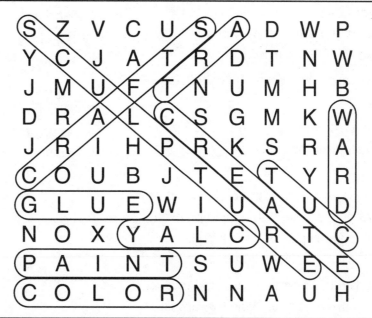

Parent Pointers

Dear Parent(s),

Whether you are a fan of art or not, you probably know some of the benefits of developing creativity. We know, for instance, that children who are creative do better academically. It is also a known fact that creativity helps us all be better problem solvers. For these and many other reasons (just plain fun is certainly one of them!), I hope you will try to encourage your child to find time for creative projects. With this note are a number of ideas to make it easier for you to get started. Feel free to join in the fun with your child. But watch out . . . it's contagious!

_____

- Keep a box of basic art supplies readily available for your child's creativity to flow. It is hard for a child to feel creative after 45 minutes of preparation in finding the supplies needed! Items to include are: crayons, colored pencils, markers, scissors, clay, beads, macaroni, yarn, stickers, construction paper, etc.

- Encourage your child to make homemade greeting cards for all occasions. Explore various creative ideas for shape, opening, cutouts, artwork, verse and medium.

- Encourage your child to keep a travel diary of pictures, even at the prewriting stage. A drawing pad in the car can stimulate creativity and a quiet car ride.

- Pipe cleaners are a wonderful introduction to sculpture.

- Revisit your past with some paper doll practice, and you'll find your child tagging along for the ride.

- Free painting is great fun. Also check with nearby craft shops which offer help or group lessons in special types of painting like ceramics or watercolor techniques.

- Don't forget the building sets and connecting blocks. These are great for "building" creativity.

- Encourage your child to make homemade gifts for family and friends. Perhaps together you can participate with a craft of your own.

- Pick up a book on easy origami or create some of your own folded-paper creations—even paper airplanes.

- The library is brimming with basic drawing and craft books to give you ideas for a rainy day. Keep a file of your favorite ideas.

- Subscribe to a children's magazine or two which offer suggestions or patterns for art projects. Your local bookstore, newsstand or library should have a few to try before subscribing.

- Share craft ideas with friends and take turns having art class with a few neighborhood kids.

- Sculpting with clay helps children discover much about the objects they make. Keep clay ready in an airtight container, and take it out whenever your child is bored.

Teacher Tips

Attach a copy of the chart header below to a copy of the grid on page 128. You can modify the number of squares by trimming off a row or two. It is important to keep the goal achievable. Each time a class has a gener-ally cooperative day, as a group, award them with a sticker, stamp or your initials in one grid on the chart.

Bring the democratic process into play with this one. When a class fills their chart, let them vote on a favorite music activity for their award day.

Class Name

Thanks for being such a **GOOD** Listener in Music Class!

Have fun finding these words in the word search!

Teacher/Date

```
C H P Z L J S J X B N S
A I C D B T E D W O T H
V S S T E W E P T N U V
E B Y U I T L E E K H O
M E S J M P S M S B F T
H S G X C H U H W Q V Y
T O H C O R A B Z D G D
Y P B P T Q I R E U U O
H N M S K A Q I M A K L
R E N R G W U P K O T E
T I D H R W K Z E A N M
Z T Z F G N I G N I S Y
```

Words to Find

beat	instruments	music	pitch	singing
harmony	melody	notes	rhythm	tempo

Answer key on page 99.

| ☐ Practices Hard in Music Class | ☐ Treats Music Materials and Instruments with Care | ▨ Follows Directions in Music Class | ☐ Follows Rules in Music Class |

I Practice Hard in Music Class!

_____
Teacher/Date

Thank you for taking good care of our music materials and instruments!

Teacher/Date

Button or Necklace

1. Cut out and color.
2. Pin on, or . . .
3. Make a hole in the top and place string or yarn through to make a necklace.
4. Tie on and wear proudly!

Follows Directions Well in Music Class!

Teacher/Date

I follow rules in MUSIC CLASS

96

Dear Parent(s),

Your child demonstrates good participation in music class. This mosaic activity is a reward for this good behavior. Have fun making this mosaic with your child!

_____
Teacher/Date

Mosaic

1. Select three different bright colors of paper for your mosaic.

2. Cut them out in small shapes about this size.

3. Glue the shapes onto the drum close together, as tiles are in a bathroom or on a floor, to create your own colorful mosaic.

4. Display your work proudly!

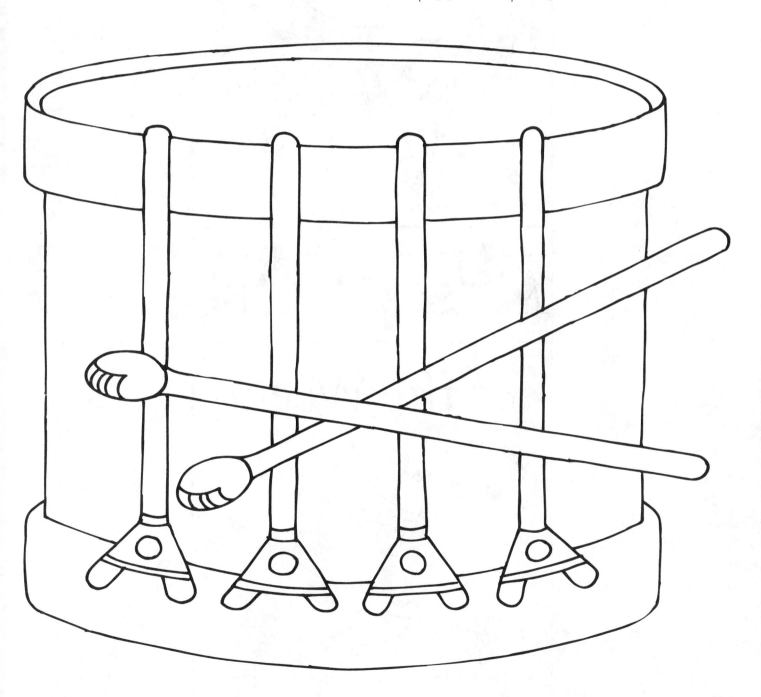

Cut along dotted lines.
Color and hang up.

MUSICIAN

of the Week!

Teacher/Date

Teacher Tips

The Music Experience

- Children learn to sing by singing! When singing with the children, choose music that appeals to their interests. Use simple accompaniments such as autoharp, guitar or piano.

- Provide a listening center where children can enjoy listening to music independently. Have a variety of tapes for children to choose from.

- Children enjoy making their own musical instruments. Try making a kazoo out of waxed paper and a comb, drums and various other rhythm instruments.

- Offer opportunities for the children to experiment with instruments to make various sounds and rhythms. Their discoveries can be the background music for a special storytelling or skit, or can enhance a song.

- Offer after-school programs such as a recorder group, choir, puppet team or drama club. Plan a special performance to show everyone what the students have learned.

- An annual talent show gives children a chance to show off their talents.

- Encourage classroom teachers to include music choices in their field trip planning, such as live concerts, theater, high school chorus or band performances and symphonies.

- You can have a greater impact on the music awareness of your preK and kindergartners if you offer a music library to these teachers to check out calming music for use during rest time.

- While listening to music, point out the sounds that are made by different musical instruments. Ask the children how the music makes them feel.

Answer Key

Good Listener in Music Class, p. 95

```
C H P Z L J S J X B N S
A I C D B T E D W O T H
V S S T E W E P T N U V
E B Y U I T L E E K H O
M E S J M P S M S B F T
H S G X C H U H W Q V Y
T O H C O R A B Z D G D
Y P B P T Q I R E U U O
H N M S K A Q I M A K L
R E N R G W U P K O T E
T I D H R W K Z E A N M
Z T Z F G N I G N I S Y
```


TLC10183 Copyright © Teaching & Learning Company, Carthage, IL 62321-0010

99

Parent Pointers

Dear Parent(s),

For many of us, music is entertainment and therapy. We relax to classic, dance to jazz and sing along with pop. You can facilitate this love for music in your own child by trying some of the suggestions below. Enjoy!

_____

Teacher/Date

- Sing in the car, in the bathtub, on a walk or when cleaning the house. It's contagious! Soon your child will mimic you and develop a love for music.

- Encourage your children or friends to create a homemade rhythm band with kitchen items and toys.

- Use sing-along tapes in the car and enjoy sing-along movies at home.

- Teach your child all the favorites from your childhood like "B•I•N•G•O" and "Old MacDonald Had a Farm." Don't forget the holiday songs. Your child will love singing along with you.

- When listening to music, let your foot tap to the beat. Can your child do this, too?

- Expose your child to a multitude of different kinds of music—country western, rock 'n' roll, barbershop quartets, classic, jazz, pop, etc. Label them each time to help your child develop an understanding of the style.

- As early as possible, give your child a tour of musical instrument stores and look at books to learn about the four different types of instruments: brass, percussion, strings and woodwinds. Help your child identify the sounds they make when you hear them.

- Allow your child to make instruments. A kitchen pot and a paper towel tube make a soft drum. A small open box with rubber bands stretched over it make a clever guitar. Use your imagination! You can have hours of fun with no cost involved.

☐ Good Behavior in P.E.   ☐ Good Participation in P.E.

Teacher Tips

Attach a copy of the chart header below to a grid from page 128. You can adjust the number of boxes in the grid by trimming off two or three rows as needed. This is important, as the age and personality of each group will bring its own unique challenge to your skills at keeping them involved. Make sure that your goal is attainable and reasonable. It won't work if it takes months to receive a reward. Each time a class is generally cooperative, reward them with a sticker, stamp or your initials in one box on the grid.

With the right reward, you can have great success at promoting generally cooperative behavior. Choose your reward according to the personality and favorite activities of each class. Possibly a free play day will be your best bet, but this may be too difficult to supervise, if activity areas are not close together. Try out a class vote to choose the day's game or activity. You could even draw a name from a hat, and let the lucky winner pick. You can gain some control over each of these approaches by offering a few acceptable choices.

Better yet, use your creativity and try something new—paper airplane making is a great lesson in aerodynamics. The kids will enjoy testing various wing and tail positions to find out which creates more distance, curves and loops. Start with one or two basic designs and then encourage the kids to experiment. Good luck!

We're Fantastic in P.E.

_____
Class Name

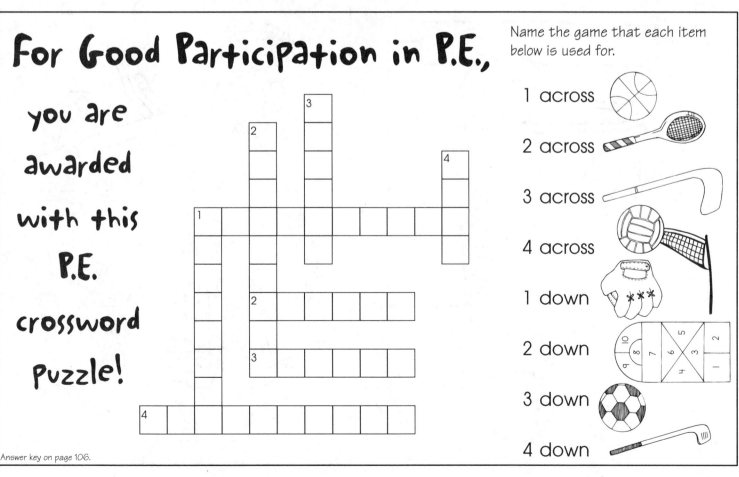

For Good Participation in P.E.,

you are awarded with this P.E. crossword puzzle!

Name the game that each item below is used for.

1 across

2 across

3 across

4 across

1 down

2 down

3 down

4 down

Answer key on page 106.

Practices Hard in P.E. ⊙ ☐ Is a Good Sport in P.E.

Dear Parent(s),

To reward your child for practicing hard in P.E., I am sending home a craft activity. This time together will further reinforce this wonderful quality, as will your praise. I hope you enjoy completing this project.

_____
Teacher/Date

Paper Cup Basketball

1. Cut the bottom out of a paper or thin plastic cup.

2. Fasten the cup to a small piece of poster board or cardboard with a brass fastener as shown.

3. Tape this hoop onto a door, wall or piece of furniture with masking tape. (It generally won't harm paint, if removed carefully.)

4. Crumple pieces of notebook or copy paper into small balls.

5. Mark your "free throw" line on the floor with masking tape, and have a free throw contest. Watch out! It's contagious!

Cut along dotted lines. Color and hang up.

I am a GOOD SPORT!

Teacher/Date

102

Dear Parent(s),

Your child follows directions well in P.E. This airplane activity should be fun for both of you to do together, and this quality time spent with your child will serve to further reinforce great behavior. Thank you and have fun!

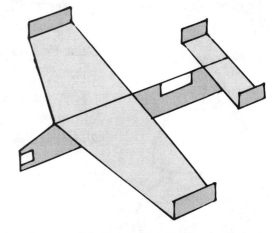

_____
Teacher/Date

Airplane

1. Color both sides of the airplane. Add windows, pilots, insignia, etc.
2. Cut out along the solid lines.
3. Fold plane upward along center fold A.
4. Tape over nose, midsection and at the end of the tail to hold the body together.
5. Fold the wings and tail down to horizontal along fold lines B and C.
6. Fold wing and tail tips up to vertical along fold lines D and E.
7. If needed, add a paper clip to the nose to add weight.
8. Let the flying begin!

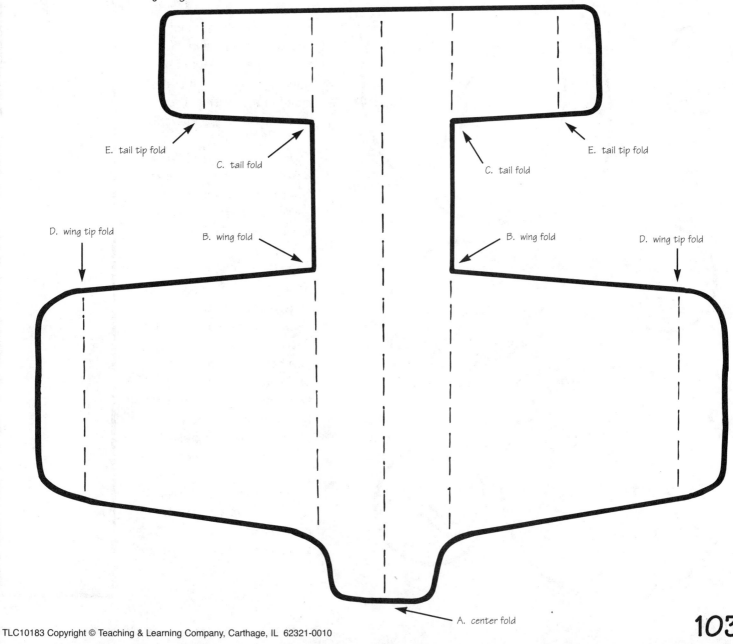

E. tail tip fold

C. tail fold

C. tail fold

E. tail tip fold

D. wing tip fold

B. wing fold

B. wing fold

D. wing tip fold

A. center fold

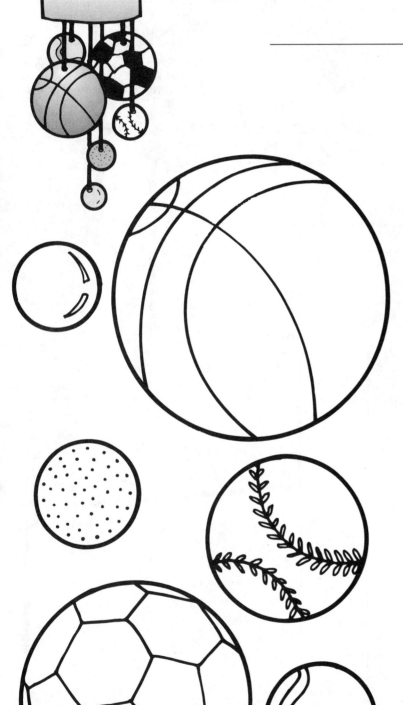

Dear Parent(s),

This sports mobile craft is a reward for your child. The ability to get along well with others in P.E. is an important skill. As you make this mobile together, please praise this wonderful quality. Thank you!

_____

Teacher/Date

Sports Mobile

1. Color and cut out the balls and the band to the right.
2. Overlap the ends of the band together into a circle and staple securely.
3. Tape three pieces of string for the top hanger inside the top of the band. Tie them together and make a hanging loop at the top.
4. Hang in a convenient low place to continue assembly.
5. Tape six pieces of string of different lengths (ranging from 3" to 10" [8 to 25 cm]) around the inside of the bottom of the band.
6. Punch a hole in each ball and tie each to one of the strings, with a loosely tied loop. The challenge is in balancing the weight distribution. Place the largest two balls on opposite sides and then experiment with the remaining four until you find a good balance of string length and ball size. This is a great science lesson, so make sure your child realizes that this is a fun challenge—one to be conquered!
7. Help your child display this award proudly.

☐ Follows Rules in P. E.   ☐ Learned to _____ Today!   ☐ Is a Pleasure to Have in Class, Because _____

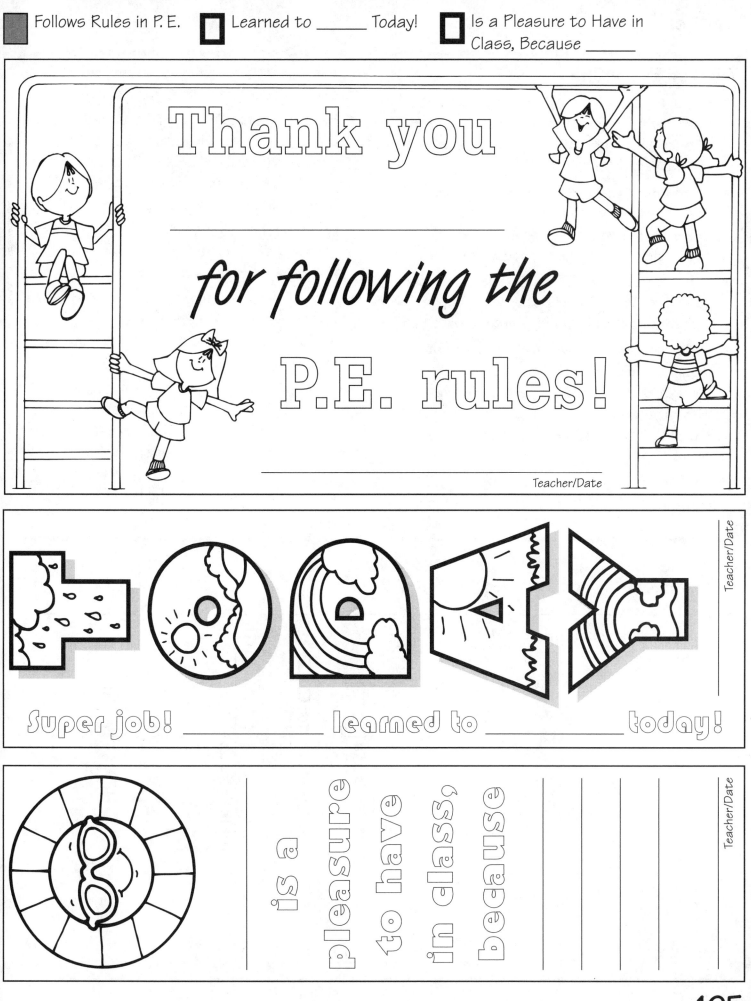

Thank you
_____
for following the
P.E. rules!

_____
Teacher/Date

Super job! _____ learned to _____ today!

Teacher/Date

is a pleasure to have in class, because _____

Teacher/Date

Teacher Tips

P.E. for Every Child

- Remember to keep your program developmentally appropriate for every child—those who are physically "gifted" and those who are physically "challenged"!

- When forming teams, consider the self-respect of every child. Try forming teams randomly based on the children's skill abilities. Don't let anyone feel left out.

- Offer clubs during P.E. class time or after school, such as running club, rope jumping club or a bowling league (by grade level).

- As a positive incentive, use your older students to help out with activities for the younger ones. These P.E. helpers can assist with physical fitness testing, setting up equipment and just being a buddy to a K-1 student.

- Find creative ways to raise money for P.E. equipment. Try a teacher dunking booth at a PTA meeting, or maybe parents will sponsor their child in a "trek" for P.E. equipment.

- Have a themed field day (Ex: country western, Olympics, carnival) to involve the whole school in physical activity. Parents love this, too. It is amazing to see the creativity flow from your volunteers on a project like this.

- Offer parents an opportunity to see their kids in action. Gymnastics night or a school track meet are just two possibilities.

- Provide various instant activities during the first five minutes of P.E. to warm up. (Ex: stretch to music, bounce ball with alternating hands)

- Build your preK and kindergarten kids' confidence with special activities just for them. One of our favorite P.E. teachers has a year-end activity for kindergarten involving a march through the whole school with a chant (Kindergarten is the best!).

Answer Key

Good Participation in P.E., p. 101

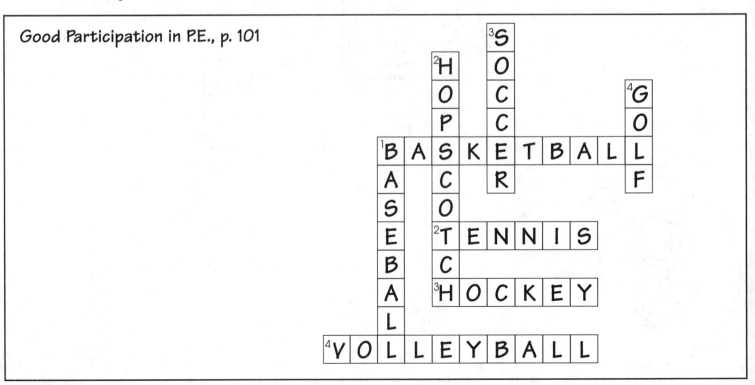

Parent Pointers

Dear Parent(s),

Learning to master one's body brings improved physical fitness and confidence to a child. Following are a few ideas you can use to help your child develop coordination and physical fitness levels. I hope you will enjoy playing right along with these fun activities!

Teacher/Date

- Help your child develop his flexibility by stretching regularly as a family. Make sure you stress the importance of stretching before and after physical activity.

- Develop your child's sense of the importance of physical activity and exercise through your own commitment. Setting an example is the strongest lesson you can give.

- If you enjoy family walks, choose a variety of places to walk, and perhaps a theme for each walk: bird watching, animal hunting, finding fall leaves, meeting neighbors, etc.

- Developing your child's coordination will help her perform better in group games at school. Hand-eye coordination is best developed through *regular* practice at throwing and catching balls of various sizes and types.

- Many games like hopscotch and three-legged races develop lower body coordination.

- Running, jogging, jumping rope, swimming and racing not only build cardiovascular strength, but just plain feel good to a kid. Encourage games that involve these activities, and take the dog jogging.

- Dancing is great exercise. Pick your music and dance the night away!

- Team sports not only build confidence and skills but also the ability to work with a team. This is a life skill that will become more important as an adult, so develop it as a child to assure maximum potential. A word to the wise parent: Let your child pick the sport and give the option to change his mind, but only *after the season is over.*

Dear Parent(s),

Your child is such a good listener in the media center that I am sending home a reward. Please take this opportunity to praise your child's fine behavior. I hope you enjoy completing this craft together.

_____
Teacher/Date

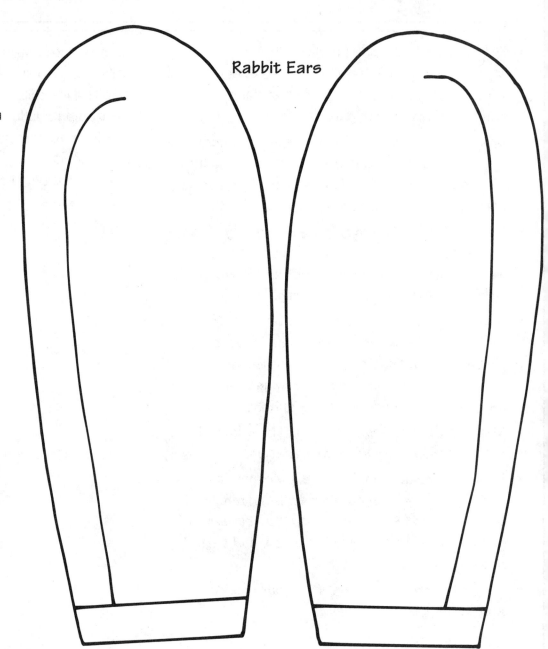

Rabbit Mask

1. Color and cut out the ears and nose/mouth of the bunny.

2. Glue these parts onto an 8" (20 cm) paper plate.

3. Draw on eyes.

4. Whiskers can be cut out of paper or drawn on.

5. To tie on the mask, punch a hole on each side of the mask. Then tie on string or yarn.

6. With big ears like this, your rabbit should be a good listener, too!
Have fun!

Rabbit Ears

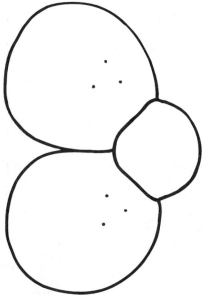

Rabbit Nose/Mouth

Teacher Tips

Attach a copy of the chart header below to a copy of the grid on page 128. Depending on the age and makeup of each group, you can adjust the number of squares in the grid by trimming off one or more rows. For each day that a class, as a group, has acceptable behavior, place a sticker, stamp or your initials in one block of the grid. Remember to keep the award attainable; it should not take too long to achieve the reward.

Free time to explore the media center is always a treat for the kids, and they often will try hard to earn this. An author or storyteller visit would be fun occasionally, or try a book hunt in small groups (of three to five). Give each group a list of five books to find or questions to answer by using the library. The first group done (correctly, of course) wins a small prize: sticker, bookmark, etc. Beware! This game leaves a few books to be reshelved. It is great fun for the kids, though, and good for their research skills.

Your older students might enjoy something a bit more challenging, like writing down call letters, after finding them in the computer or card catalog.

Class Name

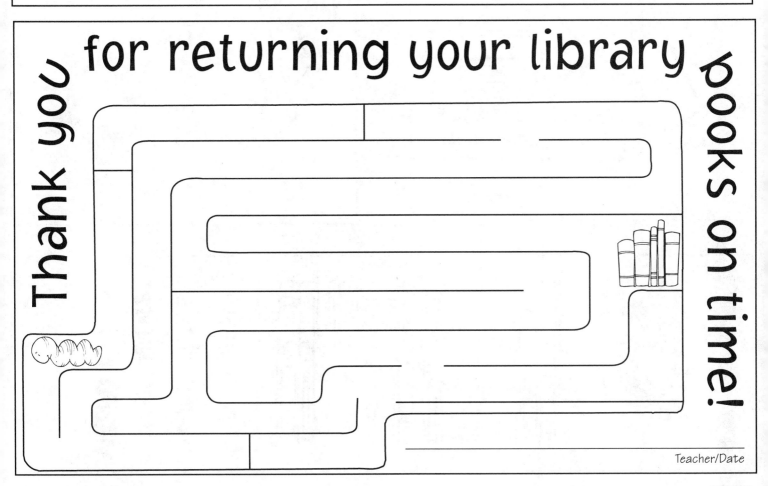

Teacher/Date

☐ Good Curiosity in the Media Center   ☐ Uses an Inside Voice in the Media Center   ☐ Follows Directions in the Media Center

Congratulations!

Curiosity in the Media Center opens the door to knowledge and reading fun!

Teacher/Date

You have earned this

Shh! Award

for using a soft voice in the Media Center. Thank you!

Teacher/Date

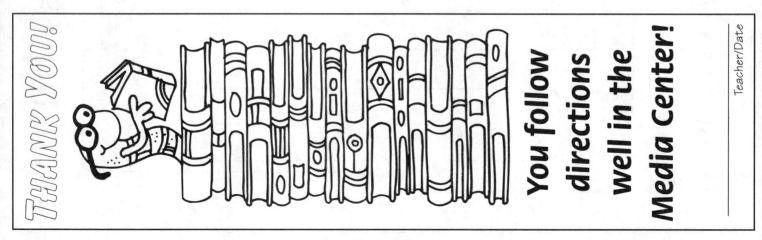

THANK YOU!

You follow directions well in the Media Center!

Teacher/Date

Dear Parent(s),

Your child now knows how to find a book in the library. This is an important skill and, as a reward, I am sending home this mobile for you to make together. Please remember to reinforce the reason for receiving this craft, I hope you enjoy it, too!

_____
Teacher/Date

Bookworm Mobile

1. Color and cut out the worm.

2. Tape the worm to a wire hanger as shown.

3. Fold two pieces of colored paper in half as shown here, and cut along fold. Fold each half in half again to make "books" for your mobile.

4. Label each little book with a favorite book title and author or a favorite kind of book. A few ideas are listed below.

5. Tape string or yarn to the inside of each "book."

6. Tie the top of the string to the hanger. Adjust the position to balance the weight so that the hanger hangs level. Enjoy!

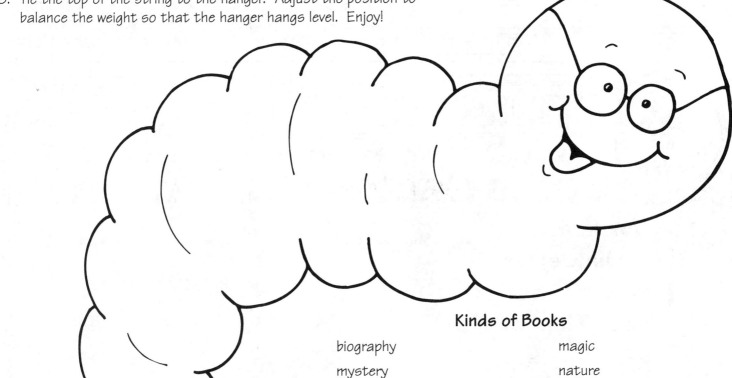

Kinds of Books

biography	magic
mystery	nature
fiction	animals
nonfiction	science experiments
science fiction	short stories
fantasy	tall tales
historical fiction	sports
jokes and humor	

You have received this

Marvelous
MEDIA
Award

*for following
Media Center rules.
Thanks!*

Enjoy this word search as your reward!

_____
Teacher/Date

Answer key on page 114.

I	B	F	I	C	T	I	O	N	Z	H	J
Z	R	I	L	J	Y	V	W	Q	I	O	N
G	S	O	O	F	U	X	K	M	K	O	M
J	T	S	M	G	M	O	P	E	I	G	Y
Y	O	C	G	U	R	X	S	T	E	W	S
S	R	E	E	P	H	A	C	F	Z	L	T
A	I	N	N	W	E	I	P	I	Y	K	E
T	E	E	D	R	F	W	H	H	X	Q	R
N	S	D	U	N	K	R	O	N	Y	S	Y
A	T	T	O	L	E	C	N	E	I	C	S
F	A	N	H	I	S	T	O	R	Y	A	H
N	X	R	U	Y	S	L	A	M	I	N	A

animals   fiction   jokes   nonfiction
biography   history   mystery   science
fantasy   humor   nature   stories

You have received this

Media Center Merit Award

**for treating
Media Center
materials with
care. Thanks.**

Make as many words as
you can using the letters
in the word **encyclopedia**.

_____
Teacher/Date

_____   _____

_____   _____

_____   _____

_____   _____

_____   _____

_____   _____

The Bookworm Award for_____

Teacher Tip

Use this award when a child finishes reading a book.

Cut along dotted lines.
Color and hang up.

has received this

BOOKWORM

AWARD

for _____

_____

_____

Teacher/Date

Teacher Tips

Building Readers

- Motivate students by having a book character or bedtime story day when children dress up. You can, too!

- Offer reading challenges by grade level, individual classes, etc., to see who can read the most Newbery or Caldecott (or any category you choose) award books. Reward their efforts.

- Form a book or reading club. Select a name that goes with your school symbol or mascot, or have the children submit their ideas and pick one. Have regular book talks or special activities for the members.

- Choose a student to read each new book and give a "book talk" on the school announcements.

- Use your imagination with small amounts of time: help small groups with research, hold a media center scavenger hunt or listen to a writer or illustrator speak about his or her work.

Answer Key

Follows Media Center Rules, p. 112

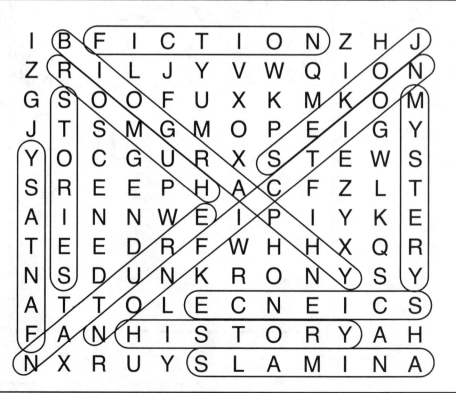

Dear Parent (s),

The library can open up worlds of interesting places to your child, but only if your child knows how to use it. Following are a few tips to help your child get started in the Media Center or library with your help. I hope you will enjoy this eye-opening experience!

_____
Teacher/Date

- Take your child to the public library regularly to browse and pique curiosity.
- Explore further topics your child finds fascinating.
- Ask a particularly friendly librarian to give you and your child a tour of the many types of materials available in the library.

- Try checking out story tapes for bedtime or documentary movies on science topics.
- Seek help on everything you do at the library, allowing your child to tag along.
- Participate in library activities such as story time and internet classes.

Teacher Tips

Copy the behavior chart header below and attach it to a copy of the grid on page 128. You can trim off one or more rows to make the award easier to earn. Keep in mind the age and activity level of each group when deciding the reward and the number of squares required to earn the reward. Each time a class has a generally cooperative day, as a group, reward them with a sticker, stamp or your initials in one of the boxes on the grid.

You are fortunate to have a built-in reward—computer time. The key here is to give choices about the activity and remove some of the structure and rules during reward time. Allow your students to pair up with friends or kids who wish to choose the same game or activity. You could even offer one rotating station of internet surfing, allowing you to supervise the sites visited. Perhaps an internet discussion with a class at another school would be fun, or e-mail another school or class. Use your imagination to create exciting rewards that will keep your kids working to earn them.

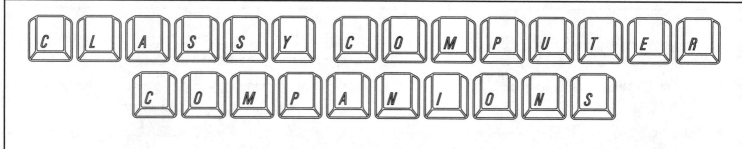

CLASSY COMPUTER COMPANIONS

_____
Class Name

You have received this

Careful Computer Operator's Award

for knowing the general rules for using the computer. Thanks!

Enjoy this word search as your reward!

_____
Teacher/Date

Words to Find

CD	keyboard	printer
CPU	modem	speaker
diskette	monitor	
internet	mouse	

M	E	S	P	E	A	K	E	R	M	C	M
O	E	T	E	F	L	M	T	N	R	E	H
N	F	S	T	L	F	E	N	F	D	I	V
I	B	C	U	E	I	G	A	O	N	D	A
T	O	K	Y	O	K	M	M	T	L	O	Y
O	J	W	L	Q	M	S	E	N	Z	D	R
R	B	T	O	W	J	R	I	D	F	Z	E
C	D	C	P	P	N	Q	J	D	N	U	T
A	Z	J	B	E	J	M	V	E	C	Z	N
F	I	U	T	C	E	X	T	D	U	D	I
R	P	J	H	P	X	S	T	L	R	V	R
C	K	E	Y	B	O	A	R	D	Y	W	P

Answer key on page 119.

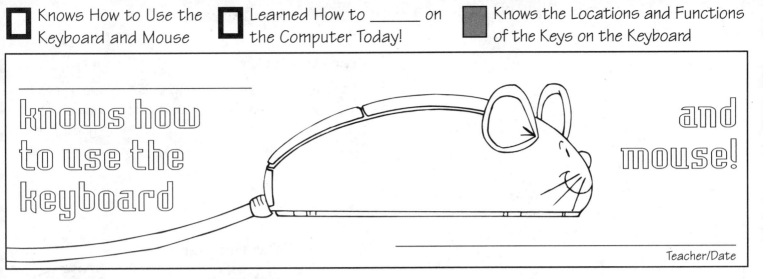

_____

knows how to use the keyboard

and mouse!

Teacher/Date

_____ learned how

to _____

on the computer today!

Teacher/Date

I know the locations and functions of the keys on the keyboard!

Ask me about any key!

Teacher/Date

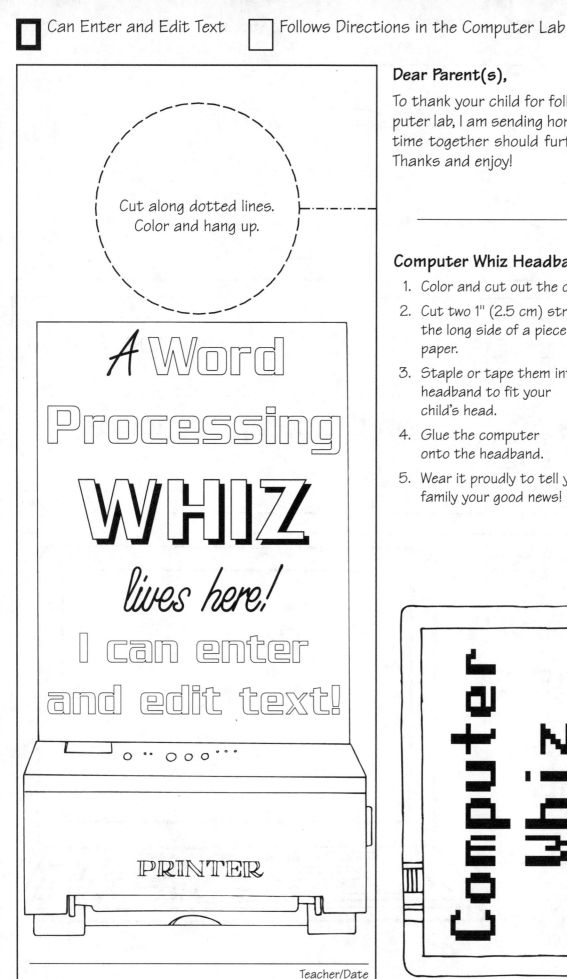

Cut along dotted lines.
Color and hang up.

A Word Processing **WHIZ** *lives here!*

I can enter and edit text!

PRINTER

Teacher/Date

Dear Parent(s),

To thank your child for following directions in the computer lab, I am sending home this headband craft. This time together should further reinforce good behavior. Thanks and enjoy!

Teacher/Date

Computer Whiz Headband

1. Color and cut out the computer.
2. Cut two 1" (2.5 cm) strips off the long side of a piece of plain paper.
3. Staple or tape them into a headband to fit your child's head.
4. Glue the computer onto the headband.
5. Wear it proudly to tell your family your good news!

Computer Whiz

Knows the General Rules for Using the
Computer, p. 116

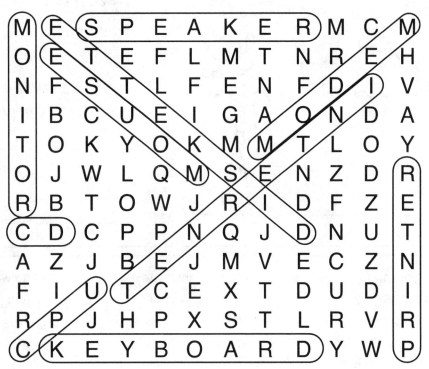

TLC10183 Copyright © Teaching & Learning Company, Carthage, IL 62321-0010

Parent Pointers

Dear Parent(s),

To be successful in the 21st century, your child needs to be computer literate. Following are a few suggestions to help you and your child make good use of your computer time. Good luck!

_____
Teacher/Date

- If you do not own a computer, we highly suggest you consider it an investment in your child's education and get one ASAP. The extra time to explore and play on the computer at home will be a great benefit later. If you cannot, consider trading time on a friend's computer for something you have to offer, or possibly taking computer classes offered for children.

- The internet is a tremendous resource and a tool that your child must master. The internet does bring some potential dangers. Consult with your internet provider to learn about blocks for certain types and categories of web sites which are inappropriate for children to happen upon. Monitor your child's use of the internet and of any buddy lists or chat rooms.

- Internet surfing should be done on a time limit, as it can easily eat up hours each day. Each time your child begins a "surfing" session, agree on a time to stop. There is always tomorrow, and such limitations will help your child be more accepting of the ones imposed at school.

- Choose a topic of interest to your child and help explore the many related sites available on the web. It is a great research tool.

- The ability to create, locate and retrieve files in a computer is essential, as is the ability to use a word processor. Word processing has already replaced its obsolete cousin, the typewriter, and is now a necessary skill for more than 65% of white and blue collar workers. As soon as your child is able, begin writing assignments and reports on the computer.

- Have your child and a friend go on an internet field trip or scavenger hunt.

☐ Can Identify the Six Primary and Secondary Colors

Dear Parent(s),

Your child can now identify the six primary and secondary colors. This is a major first step and should be celebrated. As a reward, I am sending home this mobile to make. Please help, and remember to praise your child for this new skill. Have fun!

_____
Teacher/Date

Colors Mobile

1. Color each of the paint tubes in one of the primary or secondary colors as labeled.
2. As shown, attach all parts with yarn or string, using different lengths for the paint tubes.

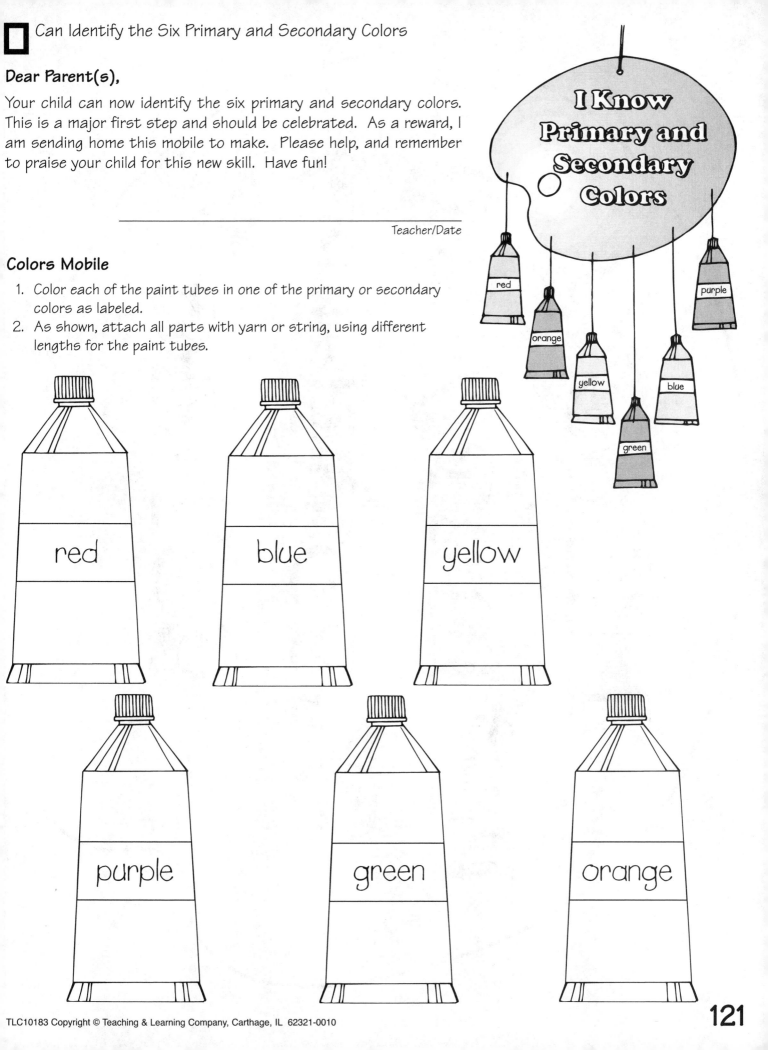

red

blue

yellow

purple

green

orange

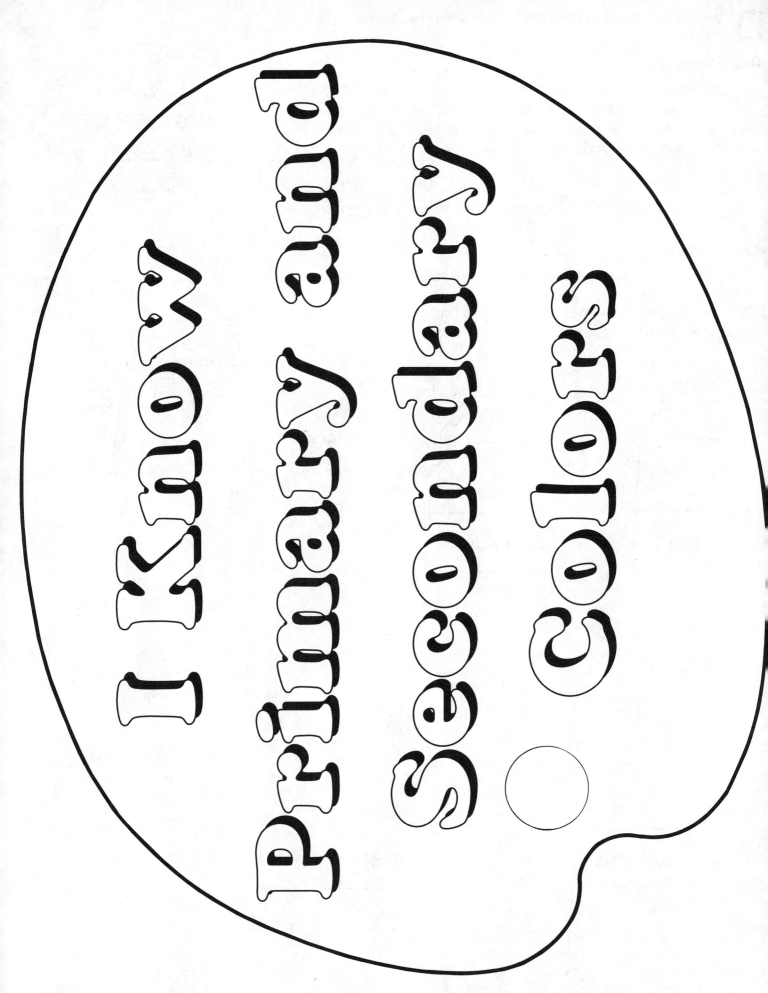

I Know Primary and Secondary Colors

Can Cut Out and Identify the Six Basic Shapes

Dear Parent(s),

Your child has mastered an understanding of the six basic shapes. Please help practice by making this shapes necklace. As you work, ask the names of the shapes and praise correct responses. Thank you!

_____
Teacher/Date

Shapes Necklace

1. Cut out the shapes and color them as labeled.
2. Punch a hole through the middle of each shape.
3. To make a necklace, lace a piece of string or yarn through each shape.
4. Tie on and have fun telling everyone the names of your shapes.

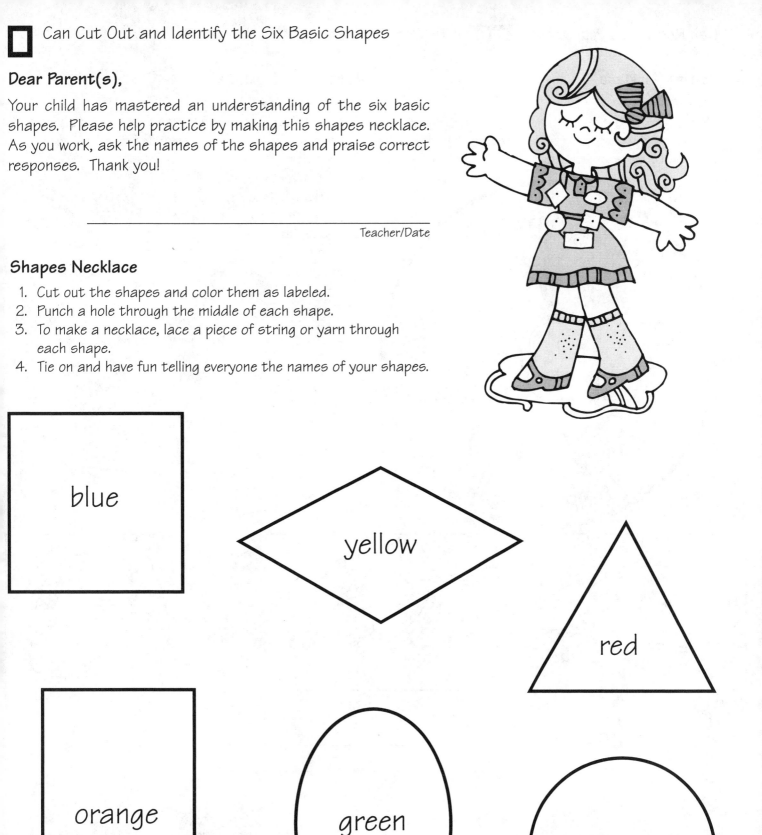

blue

yellow

red

orange

green

purple

☐ Can Recite the Alphabet   ☐ Can Tie Own Shoelaces   ☐ Can Print Own Name

Button or Necklace

1. Cut out and color.
2. Pin on, or . . .
3. Make a hole in the top and place string or yarn through to make a necklace.
4. Tie on and wear proudly!

Button or Necklace

1. Cut out and color.
2. Punch two holes where shown and thread a piece of string or yarn through the holes from the back. Tie in a bow.
3. Pin on, or . . .
4. Make a hole in the top and place string or yarn through to make a necklace.
5. Tie on and wear proudly!

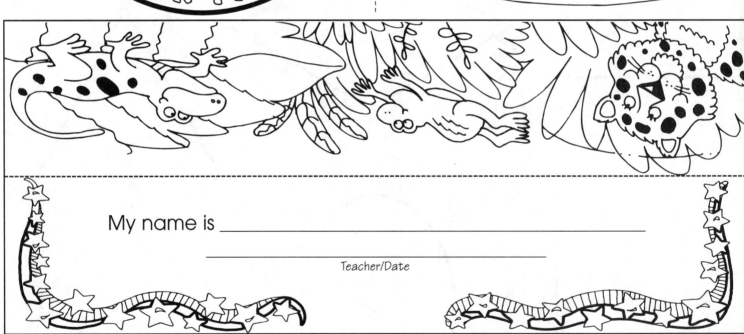

My name is _____

_____
Teacher/Date

Desk Name Sign

1. Color and write your name in large letters. Color the illustration that will be on the back.
2. Cut out the name sign.
3. Fold along the dotted line.
4. Laminate if possible.
5. Display on your desk.

Teacher Tip

This craft will last longer if laminated, and can be secured to the desk as a permanent name tag if desired.

☐ Shares School Materials

Dear Parent(s),

Help your child boast about this wonderful social skill by helping make this headband. Your child may wear it to school, if desired. I hope you enjoy this special time with your child.

_____

Teacher/Date

"I Can Share" Headband

1. Color and cut out both parts of the headband.
2. Attach the parts with tape or staples, adjusting to fit.
3. Wear with pride. You earned it!

125

Teacher Tips

PreK Teacher Tips

- Have the children talk to you about books that have been read to them (or that they have read themselves). Ask them to summarize or retell the story.

- Surround the children with a "print-rich" classroom. Label every possible object in the classroom with word labels in large print. Show them that written language is everywhere—newspapers, magazines, signs, recipes, etc.

- Provide daily practice to help children recognize and be able to name letters in upper and lowercase. Employ a variety of different practice methods and games to keep it fun. A few ideas follow:

    Bingo or lotto games allow students to practice recognizing letters and their corresponding sounds.

    Flash cards for developing alphabet understanding include letter cards, letter/picture cards and word/picture cards.

    Magnetic letters to practice "writing" words.

    Computer software programs which develop early reading skills.

    All kinds of books: alphabet books, repetitious books, word books, picture books.

- Help the children act out a story or a scene from the story using dress-up props.

- Give the children the opportunity to dictate sentences to you, so that they can see the flow of print on the page.

- Encourage the children to listen to story tapes at home and at school.

- As you read a familiar story aloud, occasionally pause to allow the children to fill in the next word or phrase.

- Expose students to nursery rhymes and read fables that teach lessons. Discuss the lessons.

- Activities such as color-watching walks, listening walks or imitating animals are fun and educational.

TLC10183 Copyright © Teaching & Learning Company, Carthage, IL 62321-0010

Dear Parent(s),

Much of what we do in preK and kindergarten is to prepare your child to be a student in first grade. This involves many social skills and skills of independence, such as tying shoelaces. Attached are a few ideas on how you might enhance our efforts here at school. Please let me know if I can help.

_____
Teacher/Date

- Helping your child understand spatial concepts contributes significantly to your child's success in preK and kindergarten. Use toys, blocks and dolls to demonstrate these concepts: in, out, around, under, through, over, on, beside and behind. When your child seems to understand, a demonstration can be given to you.

- The ability to share will assist your youngster in getting along well with others at school. You can promote this good habit with praise and a good example. Offer opportunities to share daily in your child's free play with friends, at snack time and during outdoor play. Playing catch emphasizes that sharing always gives you another chance to hold the toy.

- To help your child learn to tie her own shoes, kneel behind her and tie her shoes, first using your hands and finally using her hands.

- Any play which involves taking turns will help your child have patience at school.

- Your child's ability to get along well with playmates will become increasingly more important. Give your child frequent opportunities for free play with other children.

- Having now reached school age, your child should be encouraged to use "big kid" talk. When your child uses baby talk, teach the correct way to say the words. Praise your child's efforts!

- Encourage your child to help choose clothes each day and allow your child to dress independently. Making choices is a step toward independence. Remember that although your child's choices may not be yours, they are not life threatening. Grin and bear it!

- It is important, even at this young age, for your child to know your home address, telephone number, his or her age and birthday. Provide practice at home on these important facts. Let your child practice calling the house to learn the phone number. This will be great fun!

128   Chart Grid